MECHANIX ILLUSTRATED
HOW-TO-DO-IT
ENCYCLOPEDIA

Edited by the Combined Staffs of MECHANIX ILLUSTRATED
FAWCETT BOOKS and ELECTRONICS ILLUSTRATED

IN SIXTEEN VOLUMES

VOLUME 2

COMPLETE CONTENTS
AND INDEX IN VOLUME 16

Well-known reader services of Mechanix Illustrated are extended to readers of this encyclopedia to the extent of blueprint and plan offerings as indicated throughout the various volumes. Inquiries relating to such services and communications regarding the editorial material in this encyclopedia should be directed to Fawcett Publications, Inc., Encyclopedia Service, 67 West 44th Street, New York 36, N. Y. Printed in the United States of America.

GOLDEN PRESS • NEW YORK

Riding on Air

by Fred Russell

the pros and cons of air suspension

AIR suspension—the much-discussed arrangement that dispenses with coil and leaf springs—is quite reminiscent of the situation which existed when hydraulic brakes were first introduced. In hydraulics, we were originally faced with much too-frequent leakage of fluid. It still is a problem which apparently we are willing to endure in return for the advantages offered. In the new suspension system for cars, we substitute the problem of air leakage. With brake fluid, a one per cent water content causes a 50 degree drop in the boiling point and may bring on failure on a hot day; with air suspension, moisture may lead to icing and trouble on a cold day.

NEW-MATIC CHASSIS

The most important function of air suspension is the one least considered. While it is true that the use of special bellows under air pressure provides an appealingly cushioning effect, the outstanding advantage is the fact that cars so equipped are self-leveling. That is, they maintain the car's frame and body in a state of constant trim, there being no rear-end sag to disturb front-end alignment and to reduce suspension efficiency. This was the special feature of the torsion spring suspension system used on Packard 400 in 1955, self-leveling being done mechanically by means of a special electric motor Any car with such suspension systems will not hit bottom and, in good condition, should be able to corner with greatly reduced tendency to roll over.

There is wide difference in the details of air suspension as being offered on various makes. Briefly, the essentials include a rubber cylinder-like bellows for each wheel. Air for the bellows is supplied by a compressor driven by the car's engine. A reservoir, or accumulator, provides pressure when the engine isn't running or for extra pressure as needed. While air pressure in the reservoir may run as high as 300 pounds per square inch, it is around 110 psi for normal trim in the front "springs" of a typical car and around 70 psi for the rear. Variations in pressure are different for various makes and models.

What stands out about a properly designed and maintained air suspension system, is that springing doesn't steadily lose efficiency as happens in the case of metal springs that take a "set." But the most significant point is that air suspension puts us right back into torque drive when the whole industry was about to celebrate the triumph of Hotchkiss drive.

The Hotchkiss system is an extremely flexible way of transferring rear wheel push to the car's frame and body—and we've currently had a lot of twisting of the rear axle housing when 300 horsepower is unleashed to the driving wheels. In this type of drive the rear springs have to absorb this strain. In stopping, the braking torque is taken by the springs, too. So we get the familiar dip of the front end. With air suspension, as well as with coil springs on all four corners of the car, there must be some more rigid way of taking care of the "push" as well as the "whoa." Thus we

CLOSEUP of compressor and oil separator on one installation is shown in the photograph at the left.

PHOTO above shows high pressure tank located just behind the right rear wheel. A smaller pressure tank is behind the left rear wheel.

OWNER finds a new job in exhausting air pressure from the high pressure accumulator in photo at right.

find trailing arms on some cars to provide this positive brace between the rear axle housing and the car's frame. On one car the arms run to special extensions from the frame, while on another the arms are like wishbones on the early Fords. However, with air suspension there is no inclination to enclose the propeller shaft in torque tubes as was done for so many years on Buick and Chevrolet. This is all to the good because it makes for easier replacement of worn universals. Cars with air ride use four shock absorbers of the familiar hydraulic type—and antisway bars as well.

Whether you select air ride or conventional suspension the chances are that you will still have torque drive, because your new car will probably have four coil springs. This means that the springs, whether or not they are air bellows, will not be required to do so much work. If they are air bellows even the leveling will be accomplished automatically by special controls. They are sometimes found attached to the antisway bar up front and to torque arms in the rear. In addition, they may be controlled by door courtesy light switches as well, so that the moment Aunt Fanny gets aboard, her 300 pounds starts the suspension system leveling to compensate. Object of all this is to permit the car to maintain a normal height at all times regardless of the load or the way the load is distributed. Hence spring efficiency remains constant. This not only helps maintain braking equalization, but is most effective in keeping headlight rays properly focused at all times.

By means of a lift control, located under the dash of some cars, air pressure is allowed to push the frame and body to their top limit. This can be useful when entering a bad driveway where the car normally would hit bottom. The car must be lowered before running normally again, however. One company warns that the manual shutoff valve must either be fully open or fully closed, and that any position in between will allow some pressure loss from the system.

Here we are delving right into the matter of keeping an air suspension system perking efficiently. There are some special tricks to be learned. As with power steering, we must keep an eye on the drive belt for the compressor. On some cars this belt also drives the pump for the steering system, the power steering pump being driven by an extension of the compressor shaft very similar to the generator and water pump duo used in the old days. So in such an arrangement, if the car begins steering hard, look for belt slippage that may bring on air spring trouble, too. As with power hydraulic brakes and power steering, check all lines carefully. One of the most important service steps with the new suspension is draining of the accumulator tank. This should be done at least every 2,500 miles. The object of this is to get rid of any moisture in the system which could ice in cold

BELLOWS are fitted into metal chambers in one system; specially shaped plungers connected to suspension compress them. Load controls air fed to or released from bellows.

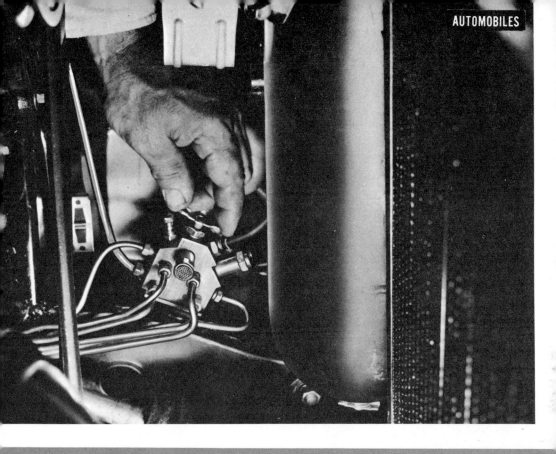

ALWAYS USE the manual shut-off valve when the car is lifted on a hoist, or for tire change.

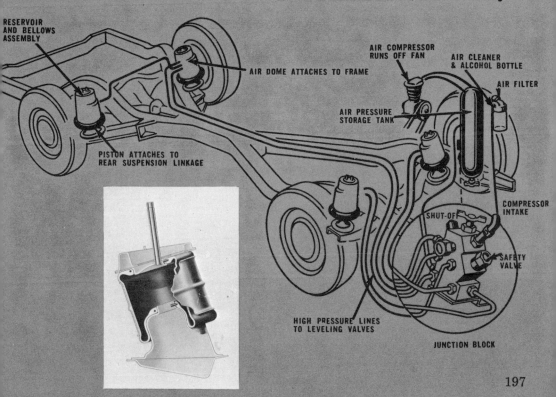

RESERVOIR
AND BELLOWS
ASSEMBLY

AIR DOME ATTACHES TO FRAME

AIR COMPRESSOR
RUNS OFF FAN

AIR CLEANER
& ALCOHOL BOTTLE

AIR FILTER

AIR PRESSURE
STORAGE TANK

PISTON ATTACHES TO
REAR SUSPENSION LINKAGE

COMPRESSOR
INTAKE

SHUT-OFF

SAFETY
VALVE

HIGH PRESSURE LINES
TO LEVELING VALVES

JUNCTION BLOCK

197

FORD suspension system is shown above. Air pressure reserve tank is under right front fender, has capacity of 400 cu. in.

FRONT SUSPENSION in Ford is essentially the same as that used with a coil spring except that an air spring is substituted.

IN CADILLAC SYSTEM, air expelled from bellows is not returned to the reservoir; instead, it is released to the atmosphere.

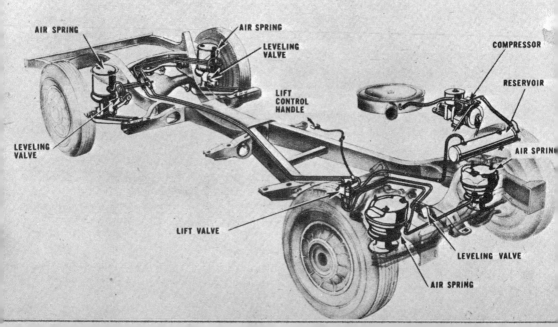

AIR LIFT chambers, sold as accessory, fit inside weakened coil springs, give support.

CLOSE-UP shows how mount for air spring is welded to the frame at the rear of a Ford.

weather. Chevrolet's system reduces icing by using a special air cleaner with an alcohol receptacle for the inlet.

Some real grief can result from failure to follow specific instructions for each make of car when jacking wheels for changing a tire, towing or merely putting the car on a lift. Crushed gas tanks and accumulators are the penalty for carelessness here. Towing instructions are given in the chapter on towing cars with automatic transmissions.

Other cautions are to jack only one rear wheel at a time when, for example, installing snow tires. On cars which have leveling controls also operated by the doors, be careful not to open a door while the car is jacked. Be careful not to raise the rear of the car when the rear shocks are removed for servicing. Overlooking this rule would result in separation of the rear air spring assemblies. In towing cars with air suspension, Cadillac recommends disconnecting the battery ground strap so as to prevent action of the leveling controls. A special point to remember is that when a wrecker is using wood supports for the towing job, the air suspension system must not be in the manual override position. You need the body's weight to keep the supports in place.

In changing a tire, instructions for several cars call for first pulling out the lift control. This raises the car's body and frame, overriding the self-leveling feature. An air suspended car will settle if it stands for several days, but if this occurs under 48 hours the system may have developed leakage. When in good working condition the air suspension system should bring the car to normal height within 5 minutes. Since air density is a factor, you will find that the time element will be greater the higher the altitude.

Troubles which may be found with these systems include failure of the car to maintain even trim, the car being tilted rearward or forward, or one front corner being higher or lower than the other. The leveling valves may be noisy. There may be slow pressure build-up or no build-up at all. The car may be too high at all four wheels. There may be too much accumulation of water in the accumulator tank. The drive belt for the compressor may jump off its pulley.

Lights On!

How to get full value
from your automobile headlights

SINCE 1939 we have been getting less than full value from our headlights even if we've kept them properly aimed and all contacts clean and tight. Why? Because in the conventional sealed beam lamp the low beam filament is not in the focal point of the reflector and the lens. Only the high beam filament enjoys this efficiency, but it is not used as much as the lower beam.

Because one filament in a sealed beam lamp is out of focus, engineers therefore decided to meet the problem by adding an extra set of lamps. This explains the current four-eyed look. Don't be surprised if this is superseded by a two-light system in which the "impossible" is done in some new and simple way. There is a hint of this in the latest improved sealed beam lamps which feature what is known as a "built-in" spotlight for better illumination of the right-hand edge of the road.

Some of the earlier cars with the four-eyed look did not carry the genuine four-

GE TYPE 1 lamp (left, photo below) has single 37½ watt high beam in focal length. Type 2 (right, below) has 50-watt low beam in optimum position. 37½-watt high beam.

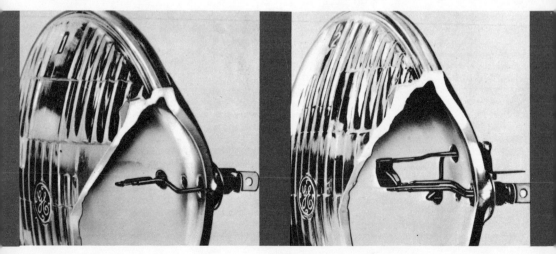

FOUR-EYED look is as much a part of today's autos as low silhouette.

UP-DATING earlier models for dual lighting done with a special kit.

SOME states have safety license plates that can be seen from a considerable distance at night.

TO AIM lamps, first remove decorative trim. Adjusting screws are then easily accessible.

lamp system, the extra lights being parking and turn-signal lamps. Because of the improvement in the low-beam focus of a genuine four-lamp system, the driver can see about 50 feet further down the right-hand side of the road. Since the lower beam is shielded, rays that would normally shoot upward are cut off, thus preventing glaring reflections from particles of dust and moisture suspended in the air. You can drive more safely in snow, rain, fog or dust with these lights. All the lamps have tabs on the lenses for mechanical aiming. Type 1 with trade number 4001 carries the upper beam, while Type 2 with trade number 4002 handles the lower beam. In addition, there is the conventional 7-inch diameter sealed beam lamp still on millions of cars. The various types are not interchangeable.

Before the new lights are aimed either by a mechanical aimer or the visual screen method, certain preliminaries are essential. First, make sure tire pressures are equalized and that the car is on a flat, level surface. Since there may be some binding in shackles or shock absorbers always rock the car up and down and side-to-side to free it up. No passengers should be aboard at the time, and the luggage compartment should carry only the normal equipment. Lamps should be checked for brilliance by running the engine fast enough to bring the generator into full output. Sometimes a a bad connection is all that is necessary to bring the lights back to normal again. Clean the lenses, of course, and also the aiming pads which are molded into the face of each lens. Aiming bosses on the sealed beam unit lenses have a flat surface. If these are damaged they should be replaced.

Use of Aiming Screw

Your mechanic will take off the trim around the headlamps, thereby uncovering the retainer ring and the adjustment screws. The aiming screw at the top or the bottom of the lamp is the one he will use for vertical adjustment, the one at the side

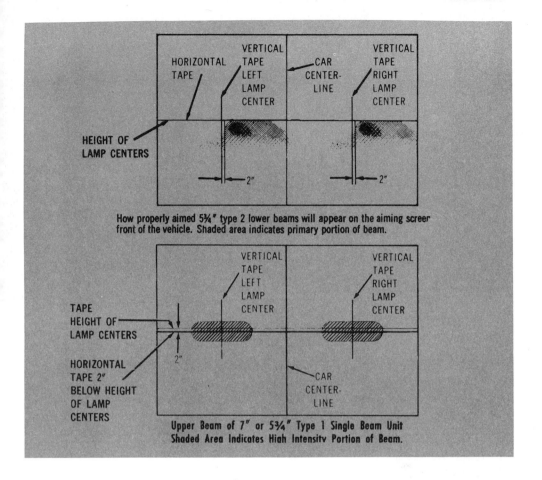

How properly aimed 5¾" type 2 lower beams will appear on the aiming screen
front of the vehicle. Shaded area indicates primary portion of beam.

Upper Beam of 7" or 5¾" Type 1 Single Beam Unit
Shaded Area Indicates High Intensity Portion of Beam.

of the lamp being for the horizontal adjustment. Mechanical aimers can be used in broad daylight since the lamps need not be switched on during the process.

While it is possible to aim lamps by the visual screen method it is just a lot of work which any smart motorist would wisely duck, knowing the pitfalls such as failing to aim the Type 2 lamps correctly, because of not accurately locating the top and left side of the area of the lower beam's high intensity. You would need a screen, a center-line-of car painted on a level flooring, movable hooks, weights and springs to provide the guide lines on the screen, and considerable know-how. It's like using two bumper jacks to lift the rear of the car, when Joe at the corner filling station can do the job in a tenth of the time with his hydraulic jack.

But you'll want to know how the light patterns should look if the lights are subjected to official inspection. The accompanying chart will show how things should

look for both lower beam and high beam lamps, together with tolerance limits plus and minus. Note that the aim for the Type 1 single beam lamp used in the four-lamp systems is the same as for the conventional 7-inch lamp's upper beam.

The primary gain which the newer system offers is improved lighting with the lower beam which is the one you use most of the time. A conventional dimmer switch gives you choice of low beam only or the high beam which brings into action all four lights. The Autronic Eye can be used with the new as well as the older systems. This is the automatic dimming device which incorporates an electronic eye. As soon as the headlights of an approaching car (usually about 1000 feet ahead) come into view, the lights on an Autronic Eye equipped car drop instantly to the low beam lamps until the other car passes. There's a special switch by means of which the driver can override automatic action any time he feels the need to. •

Looking For Trouble

You'll find it saves time and money in the long run

EVEN though you're likely to find trouble if you go looking for it, the automotive philosopher points out the additional fact that you'll also find relief from breakdowns and major repair bills. To him looking for trouble is the shortest cut to looking for the silver lining.

He is the high priest of preventive service. Constantly feeling the car's pulse he is quick to note anything that isn't as it should be. Of course he knows a false alarm when he hears one, and if the car is in-

dulging in some puzzling bit of misbehavior he doesn't rush to the repair shop. But since the little things do not escape his notice he finds it easy to avoid being caught red-handed with real woes.

I recall watching him as he cranked the engine one morning. Most drivers are so intent on where they are going with the car they give no thought to the cranking process, and so would not be likely to note that the cranking speed was way below standard. "I drove enough yesterday to

WIRE BRUSH is used to clean battery posts.

POWER STEERING belt is checked for tension.

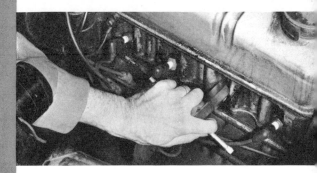

LOOSE SPARK PLUGS should be tightened down.

OIL can accumulate around a loose spark plug.

charge even a weak battery," he observed. "The generator is charging, and the battery isn't old enough to have developed an internal leak. That gives me a clue."

With that he headed for the corner filling station where he asked Joe to remove the battery terminals and clean them with a wire brush. "You'd be surprised how much trouble you can get into with corroded or just dirty battery posts and terminals," was his only comment. But it explained why we ought to listen carefully every time the engine is cranked.

This got us off to a good "start" on the timely business of inspecting as you go. While the hood was raised, and the engine still quite cool, Joe decided to check the water level in the radiator. Finding it lower than it should have been he felt the hose from the bottom of the radiator to the engine and found it to be soft. "It's collapsing when the pump starts really sucking at 35 miles per hour and over," he decided. "That's the way I liked to catch trouble—red-handed." But before replacing the cap Joe also felt around the outside of the filler pipe's neck. It was rough enough to suggest that the cap probably was pretty well worn. "I'll smooth this off and install a new cap before you have trouble come hot weather," he announced with a knowing wink.

It remined me of the day I decided to take a look at the tire walls which face the car. You know we spend much time looking over the exposed whitewalls, and bemoaning the fact that we scrape them too often against the curb, yet ignore the other side where tires so often develop dangerous cuts. This time I found nothing wrong with the tires themselves, but on the left rear tire there were signs of leaking brake fluid. Pulling back the rubber boots over the brake cylinder ends confirmed the fact of leakage. Then there was the day I decided to check top speed before the transmission went into high, trying this on a hill just to prove my point with more certainty. I was not especially pleased when the engine started to miss around 40 miles per hour, but I had to admit it was better than being caught with a weak, failing fuel pump a few days later when I would have been trying to roll up 400 miles a day in the sort of hot weather when pump diaphragms are more likely to fail anyway.

Looking for trouble goes a long way toward getting better results from many of the car's most important units. If your mechanic has one of the new windshield wiper arm pressure gauges which the

DIP STICK is checked to determine the oil level. The odor of the oil sometimes may indicate presence of harmful contaminants.

HIGH-SPEED SHIMMY can be caused by a badly worn universal joint on drive shaft.

AUTOMATIC CHOKE that fails to open fully can knock your gas mileage for a loop.

REPAIR radiator leaks immediately, then check water level at regular intervals.

VAPORS from oil filler pipe may indicate clogged crankcase vents or oil dilution.

Anderson Company makes, ask him to check the wipers on your car. Pressure should be one ounce per inch of wiper blade length. A 12-inch blade therefore should bear against the glass with 12 ounces pressure. If it doesn't measure up to this standard there will be trouble ahead. Either the wipers will tend to scratch the glass and be slow moving, or they will not bear heavily enough and will streak the glass or lift off when wind is high.

You'll really need to be a sleuth with this business. Take the matter of checking the fuel filter. Finding water, one motorist seemed to feel so relieved when he emptied it out. What he should have done was to take a look at the bowl a few days later to see if it was trapping any more water.

Had he done this he would have discovered that there was a lot of water in the gas tank. It causes a real tie-up during a cold spell. Finding nothing wrong with front-end alignment when his car developed a high-speed shimmy, another motorist wisely checked the universal joints and found them badly worn. The front end was being disturbed by propeller shaft whipping.

Especially with self-sealing tires, it isn't enough to check treads for embedded nails or other sharp objects which ought to be removed. In addition, when checking any kind of tire it pays to run the palm of your hand over the tread to spot any worn areas. They are often a sign of faulty braking or, if on front tires only, worn spots may be proof that there is excessive pivot-

BRAKE FLUID dripping on inside walls of rear tires can effect serious damage.

ROCK car's rear end to determine if sagging springs cause that front-wheel shimmy.

MOTOR MOUNTS should be tightened occasionally to cut down on motor vibrations.

FUEL PUMP can be checked by high-speed operation of the car's engine in low gear.

ing. One of the best opportunities for demonstrating this theme is willingness to allow filling station folk to "check your oil." You just never know what will be discovered when the hood is raised even though the oil supply will not need any additions. A little oil around the well of a spark plug hints of need for tightening. A loose belt for the power steering pump may be the start of trouble. Vapors coming up from the oil filler pipe hint of possible clogging of the crankcase vents, badly diluted oil, or worn piston rings.

Watch the engine, too, as it idles before slamming down the hood. If it shakes too much, idling speed may be set too low. Continued shaking as you accelerate the engine, hints of loose motor mounts—provided there isn't some obvious missing that would be due to ignition misbehavior or valve trouble. When an engine backfires during starting put it down as a valve condition. One of the intakes hangs up momentarily, allowing its respective cylinder's charge to fire back through the carburetor into the air cleaner. Sometimes this is an indication of a too lean carburetor mixture, but if the choke is found to be working normally look for badly worn intake valve guides in an engine that has seen a lot of service.

One reason why it is so important to search out the real cause of a car's ailment is to head off complications. You may be willing to put up with trouble starting the engine but consider how much crankcase dilution develops because of a sluggish choke. Currently there's a tendency to take poor gas mileage in our stride just because everyone else is complaining about it. But suppose we face up to reality and consider the possibility that in our own particular case inefficiency may be due to low compression, a weak coil or a sluggish thermostat? How about defective gaskets and worn linkage in the carburetor itself?

Sometimes, too, we invite trouble by too much willingness to put up with what seems like a minor form of it. That "pinging" of the engine may seem to be merely lost performance from not using high enough octane gas, but what of the risk of cracking a spark plug's insulator? What of the extra strain on the pistons and bearings? What of the increase in engine temperature on a hot day? All this has to be taken into account, not merely taken in our stride.

The smart caper seems to be to choose your own time for the trouble hunt and to conduct it under your own terms. As some sage may have wisely observed, "Better to look for trouble than to have trouble look for you."

TIRE DEFECTS not clearly visible may be detected by running your hand over tread.

WATER in fuel filter bowl may originate in gas tank. Full tank cuts down condensation.

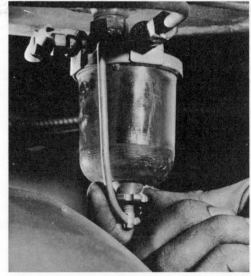

Cockeyed Wheels

Much car trouble is merely a matter of misalignment

BECAUSE trouble with front-end alignment so often can be seen in the odd ways front tires wear, millions of motorists have lapsed into the expensive habit of assuming that if the treads show no abnormal wear everything is well with the car's prow. Your brand new Elegant Eight as well as your neighbor's Snappy Six prove that nothing could be further from the truth.

When one motorist rushed to the repair shop to complain about feeling enough road shock to suggest a pair of broken shock absorbers, he even pictured a broken coil spring or a bent wheel spindle. But his mechanic calmly sat down to a cup of coffee and announced that after his morning "break" he would put the car on the alignment machine. "It looks to me like too much caster or negative camber," he explained. "Funny how so much car trouble boils down to misalignment."

He went on to tell about another customer whose car developed the bad habit of steering in an erratic way whenever brakes were applied. It began to look a bit mysterious when a careful check on braking failed to show up anything wrong in the deceleration department. Again the mechanic nodded in the direction of his alignment machine. "You're ahead of me if you have figured that this steering condition was found to be the result of too little caster," he added. "Even unequal caster will do this."

In these cases there was no hint whatever of tire wear. You would never have suspected there was anything wrong with

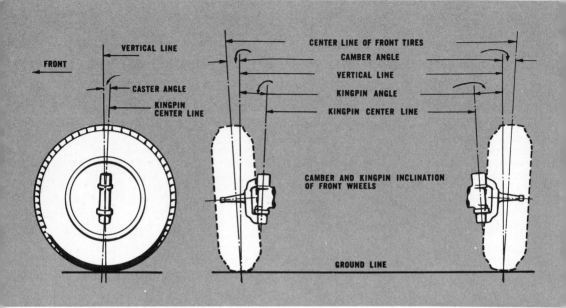

VERTICAL LINE

FRONT

CASTER ANGLE

KINGPIN
CENTER LINE

CENTER LINE OF FRONT TIRES

CAMBER ANGLE

VERTICAL LINE

KINGPIN ANGLE

KINGPIN CENTER LINE

CAMBER AND KINGPIN INCLINATION
OF FRONT WHEELS

GROUND LINE

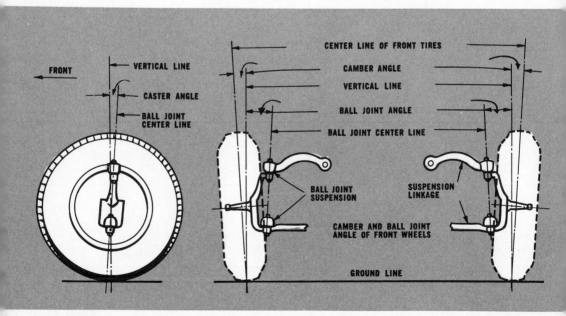

FRONT

VERTICAL LINE

CASTER ANGLE

BALL JOINT
CENTER LINE

CENTER LINE OF FRONT TIRES

CAMBER ANGLE

VERTICAL LINE

BALL JOINT ANGLE

BALL JOINT CENTER LINE

BALL JOINT
SUSPENSION

SUSPENSION
LINKAGE

CAMBER AND BALL JOINT
ANGLE OF FRONT WHEELS

GROUND LINE

alignment, yet it was the sole cause of the trouble. It reminded me of the case of a car that became increasingly harder to steer. "A loose steering gear case," said one mechanic. Disagreeing was a shop foreman who suggested too tight adjustment of ball joints. A third came out with the idea that the particular model car was known to develop steering column distortion. It seemed to be adding up to an expensive mess of repairs with no one being too sure of the outcome. But my friend was smart. He recalled that the car hadn't been treated to a wheel alignment in over a year, and with only this much to bank on he decided to knock a hole in a ten dollar bill by having a front-end alignment expert look over the situation.

Correcting for too much caster and toe-out the alignment man came up with a quick remedy for a seemingly serious steering situation. It was like giving someone who's ill a comfortable bed and a glass of water even if you don't know exactly what's ailing him. The mere rest may bring him out of it. A car that was darting and diving all over the road could have had eccentric wheels or a bent king pin, but a basic alignment job showed that the only fault was excessive toe-in.

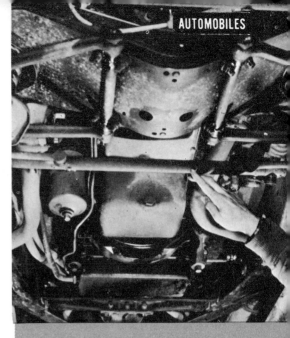

DRAG LINK should be inspected. If bent, it will throw the wheels out of alignment.

ILLUSTRATIONS shown across page should be studied carefully, explain alignment.

OUT-OF-BALANCE wheel may cause shimmy, so add counterweights to rebalance.

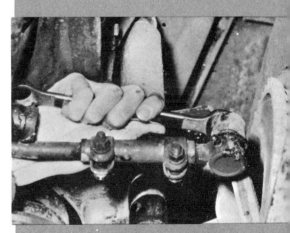

LOOSE TIE ROD sockets (above) should be greased and then tightened down. Steering connections (below), if loose or binding, can also be a cause of misalignment

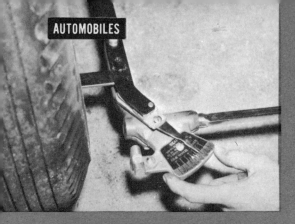

WHEEL ALIGNMENT indicator will give you a true picture of that out-of-true wheel.

PORTABLE wheel aligner ("weegee board") is used to measure the amount of toe-in.

The newer features on cars tend to cover up these basics, but don't let them fool you. Recently a driver noticed that his car started wandering and weaving. Naturally he jumped to the conclusion that something was amiss with the power steering system. Someone put him wise to the fact that there might be trouble with the front end, so he made a date with an alignment man who seemed to be wasting time checking front tires for pressure. Finding these at the correct pressure, he then surprised the owner by checking the rear tires, too. And right there he proved himself to be a smart mechanic. One of the rear tires was way down, due to a rim leak. It threw front-end caster way off on one side of the car only, giving a most uncomfortable steering effect.

Many drivers do not realize that shimmy is one of the most certain proofs of alignment trouble, if it is the low-speed variety coming in when the car is traveling 35 mph or less. At higher speeds misalignment may be the cause, but here tire and wheel unbalance are likely to have priority. Too much caster can bring on quite a front-end hula-hula, and this caster excess may be due to the rear end of the car sagging. Too many people in the car, and too much luggage, are the chief causes of such sag. New-type shock absorbers are designed to compensate for this automatically. The new air-spring suspensions are another important step in the right direction.

When high-speed shimmy persists in spite of properly balanced wheels and tires, the trouble may be the same excessive caster (in which case the front wheels will go into their gyrations at almost any car speed), but in addition the shimmy may be due to excessive toe-in or toe-out. So whether or not there is any hint of misalignment as revealed by oddities in tire wear, it pays to head for an alignment shop if any of the conditions I have mentioned come your way.

And it will help if you have some idea of what he is doing to the front end. His equipment varies widely but all he is trying to find out is the situation with respect to eight features of what is known as steering geometry. The first four are discussed a lot wherever car fanciers meet, even though the particular elements of alignment may not be fully understood. Mention toe-in to the motorist of reasonable experience and he understands that this means the front wheels are closer together at their fronts than at their rears. He knows, too, that camber means the outward tilt of the wheels although he may not understand that the idea of this is to bring the center of each front tire tread as near as is possible for it to be directly under the point of load. The third element—caster—immediately brings a picture of those little wheels on the legs of heavy furniture, but not many realize that the backward tilting of the front wheels not only eases steering but helps them run straight. Then, fourth, we have toe-out which applies only on turns. If it weren't for this the inside wheel would be dragged during a turn.

But the other four points to be considered in the overall alignment picture are less familiar and it requires no imagination to see why a mechanic these days can't check alignment like he would inspect the oil level in the crankcase. He has to know all the angles to what is known as "king pin inclination." That is, king pins must tilt outward at the bottom. If it weren't for this we'd have to risk setting the wheels for too much camber. Right here let's pause to reflect over the fact that the five elements so far mentioned serve a common purpose in what might be considered a merging of pivots. Here's how you can keep this in mind for the rest of your motoring career:

Hold your hands and arms outstretched, palms facing and a foot apart. For purpose

LUBRICATION of all steering components is important, particularly the gear box.

of comparison your hands are then your car's front wheels. Now move the fingers of one hand a little closer to those of the other to represent toe-in. To get the camber effect turn the lower edge of one hand nearer to that of the other, but without changing the "toe-in." Next—to introduce caster—tilt your hands a bit so that the fingers are higher than your wrists. If you will swing your hands from the wrists right or left to simulate turning around a curve you will not find it difficult to believe that the inner wheel will turn in a smaller arc but at a higher degree of turning radius. The longer the car's wheelbase the less toe-out; the wider the tread (distance between wheels) the more the toe-out.

Ball Joint Setup

Ball joints which on many cars now replace the conventional knee-action design and kingpins is a simpler arrangement, the lower ball joints carrying car weight. Upper ball joints are merely guides, and rubber bushings are used at the inner ends of the upper and lower control arms. The net effect is that two ball joints replace the five bearings previously found at each front wheel. Ball joints are found to be more durable than pins and bushings, and service is simpler.

I like a popular expression which also helps get the picture of the pivoting elements of alignment. If you were pigeon-toed and had bow-legs you would be in correct alignment if you walked leaning a little backward.

Merely checking pivot points and correcting for errors is, however, no assurance of perfect alignment. Important to the picture is wheel and tire balance because of the close relationship between the way the tires spin and the manner in which the wheels pivot when meeting various steering conditions, load, and road shock. This inter-relationship calls for making sure that the rear wheels are parallel with the

ones up front. This is what the alignment man means by "tracking."

Finally, there is "steering control alignment"—the complete situation existing between the steering wheel and the movement of the front wheels. It calls for checking not only the steering gear but all of the steering linkage. Here your mechanic will look for such irregularities as a bent drag link, distortion of the steering column, loose tie-rod sockets, loose steering arms and loose or binding steering connections. He will also make certain that the steering gear itself is adjusted on its high spot or on a new high spot if the car has been kicking around for some time. Here lubrication is important because often there is leakage around the gearcase gaskets. Every now and again cars are found with a loose steering gear case. The owner complains that he finds it difficult to hold the car on a crowned road and assumes that alignment is suffering.

Shock absorbers that need fluid will invite temporary misalignment, and because fluids vary in viscosity during temperature changes a car that steers to perfection at 10 degrees below may not be so pleasant to drive at 90 in the shade or vice versa. Trouble with rear shock absorbers will also adversely affect the front end's health. So will weak or a broken rear spring. And don't forget that the front coil springs can cause a lot of trouble if weak and thus sagged.

When air springs become as common as power steering we'll be including them in the alignment picture. Chief troubles are air leakage and incorrect leveling. Here we discover that front-end alignment trouble can develop under the hood at the air pressure pump or in the lines and connections.

Traveling too fast over rough roads is a short cut to knocking wheels into misalignment. It is worse than hitting the curb because it is done at much higher speed and may be repeated many times in the course of even a mile of travel High-speed turns put great strain on the front end, and there is the habit of forgetting to have the car greased. And the subject is not complete without a word for two common conditions which may make the car most unsatisfactory to drive. One is tramp or thump from a faulty tire. This can't be eliminated by balancing. It calls for truing —a process of buffing off the high spots. Sounds like a wasteful process but it actually prolongs the life of any tire so afflicted. The other condition is an eccentric wheel. Sloppy manufacture or damage to the wheel brings on this one. Replacement is the only answer. •

On the Firing Line

Cleaning and setting spark plugs is a precision job

KNOWING the engine's special needs before tackling spark plugs can pay real dividends.

PLUGS show normal wear (left) at high and (right) at low speeds; both need a cleaning.

CARBON DEPOSITS (left) indicate over-rich mixture, dirty air cleaner. Try using hotter plugs if you notice that oil accumulates (center); or cooler ones if your plugs overheat (right).

SOMEWHERE under the mess of pipes, cables, manifolds, tubes and wires is a familiar part of the engine which has been perking away since Detroit was a one-lunger. It is none other than the trusty spark plug—if you can find it in that maze of gadgetry which we have come to know as the modern automobile's power plant.

The spark's not everything, but mighty close to it. If weak or slightly intermittent it not only produces poorly fired mixture but, handicapping the engine, may put a crimp in the behavior of the car's automatic transmission. Turning this inside out we see the condition of spark plugs as an indication of the engine's troubles or needs. I saw this illustrated when a mechanic looked over plugs that were badly burned. It looked like evidence of excessive speed, but that wasn't the story at all. A further check showed that the engine was suffering from a long period of overheating, late ignition timing being the real cause. On another set of plugs the points were all fouled up with oil, although the engine was normally warmed up at the time. Things had all the earmarks of a situation wherein the plugs were too cool a type either for the engine or the limited way in which the car was customarily operated. But here's what the repairer found:

First thing that caught his eye was an extremely dirty oil filler pipe. That could mean clogged crankcase vents and badly diluted oil. Checking the oil and finding it dirty seemed to confirm this, but he next decided to take a compression reading of the cylinders. Just as he suspected they were all way below par, suggesting sticky or worn piston rings. A third check showed that the windshield wipers slowed down when the engine was accelerated. A leaky diaphragm in the booster side of the pump was allowing oil to suck into the cylinders.

Thus we get a surprisingly fine check on what's what with the engine when we take out the plugs and see how they look. But, first of all, where are they? Some are sunk in wells. To find the plugs on the right bank of one engine you've got to remove the heater duct and blower assembly. Some are covered with a metal plate. But let's consider a few points before actually removing the plugs.

Cleaning plugs externally will help check condensation which so often allows high tension current to jump externally. Poor terminal contacts place an extra load on the ignition coil. Poor wiring may mean occasional plug starvation, remembering that wiring often breaks inside its insulation. Another point to note is how the ignition cables are positioned in their route from the distributor to the plugs. Some have an unusual crossover to prevent what is known as "Cross-firing." Some real goofy engine operation has followed failure to replace wires in exactly the way the engineers originally positioned them. It is

SOAK old plugs in solvent, then clean threads with a stiff brush and wipe dry.

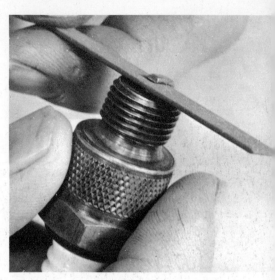

FILE points until bright, being sure to clean away the filings before replacing the plugs.

more than a matter of making sure the wires reach their plugs in correct sequence.

Next step is to clean all dirt and foreign matter from around the plugs before unscrewing them. If you have a tank type vacuum cleaner handy you can remove the hose and blow dirt from the plug wells most effectively; otherwise just use a small brush and carefully wipe out the well with a clean cloth. Signs of oil around the plugs hint of looseness and will serve to head off jumping to the conclusion that oily deposits on the plugs and extra carbon in the cylinders mean that the rings are shot. A number of cars have heater ducts which must be removed to get at some of the plugs. Or you may need to remove the generator to get to one particular plug. If there are cover plates be careful not to buckle them by overtightening when they are replaced. If the car is equipped with air conditioning and a compressor for air springs some additional roadblocks are likely to be encountered, but let's get on with the story by tackling a motor where the plugs are sunk into relatively deep wells with an insulating sleeve over each plug and its nearby wiring. These sleeves are disconnected by merely gripping their ends and pulling. A deep socket of 13/16 size with a 9-inch extension is needed to loosen the plugs. Then they can be withdrawn by lifting out the metal cylinder known as the mounting "cam." Plugs on other engines are easily removed with the right size hex top socket, once you have

cleared away the brush and are ready for business.

Especially important when removing plugs is to place them in some improvised holder so as to indicate the number cylinder from which they were taken. Thus if there is some unusual condition which any particular plug reveals you'll know which cylinder is involved. If one plug shows a badly fused or blistered insulator, for instance, there may be water leaking into its particular cylinder. An oily plug that was not loose when you started removing it might hint of ring trouble in that particular cylinder.

Plug threads are now cleaned with a wire brush, and oily deposits removed with a solvent such as alcohol. Removing carbon from the electrodes is fairly easy but the same cannot be said for the insulator. Here cleaning with solvent and a knife is hardly worth the effort and may result in damage. Better take the plugs to your filling station and have them clean the insulators in their special blast machine. Plugs should be subjected to blasting not more than six seconds each, and should be "wobbled" during the process.

You can then use a thin flat file on the electrodes, the object being to make their surfaces bright, as flat as possible and parallel. Don't be afraid to be vigorous in filing. For accuracy in resetting the plugs for proper gapping, be sure you use a round feeler gauge. It's very important that the gap between electrodes be exactly

SPARK PLUG adjusting tool has a full set of wire feeler gauges and other attachments used on plug repair jobs. Here a wire gauge is being used to measure gap accuracy.

ROUND feeler gauge is used to set the gap of the plug's electrodes to the manufacturer's specifications. Bend only the side electrode, then recheck gap with gauge.

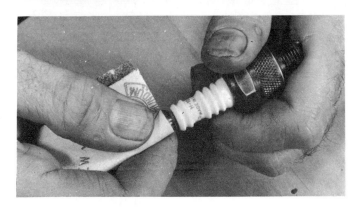

CENTER ELECTRODES should be brightly polished and thoroughly cleaned before replacing plugs. Shine them with a piece of fine-grain sandpaper, then wipe clean.

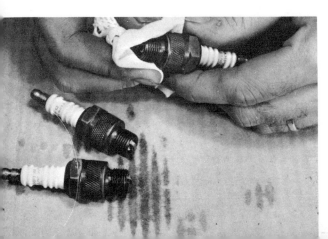

WHEN SPARK PLUGS have been thoroughly cleaned and dried they should be tested against new ones on a comparator machine before being re-installed in your engine.

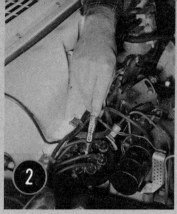

SOME LAST-MINUTE CHECKS: (1) A final dusting of spark plug electrodes. (2) Checking plugs with a pin-point tester. (3) Wiping clean all connections on the distributor cap.

what the manufacturer of your car recommends for the particular model engine.

Should the old plugs be used again?

That's important, even though your neighbor has used the same plugs for 30,000 miles and thinks he is doing himself a service. With today's engine performance it may be necessary to discard a set of plugs at 8,000 miles or even less. Much will depend on how well the plugs match not only the engine's basic characteristics but the way the car is driven. Whether the type plug in the engine is right for these conditions will be decided by the appearance of the old plugs when you take them out and look them over. If plugs are being overheated you'll know it by badly eroded points and a white or blistered nose on their insulator. Here switch to a cooler type plug, going just one step toward the cool side. Your dealer has a plug chart to help with the selection. But be on your guard. If only a few of the plugs look this way there may be trouble such as an air leak in the intake manifold. Think back, too, over the way the engine has been acting. If it has been pinging and overheating it needs a motor checkup, not necessarily new plugs.

Oily deposits on plugs can be the result of a lot of engine conditions including worn rings, a leaky vacuum booster of the dual type fuel pump, too high oil pressure, or worn valve stem guides, but if you can't seem to locate a definite cause try a set of hotter plugs. New engines may foul up their plugs during the break-in period which is why a cleaning is advisable at 2,000 miles or so. Heavy carbon deposits on the plugs mean an overrich mixture from such conditions as trouble with the automatic choke, too much city driving, a dirty air filter or a high carburetor float level. Here again, assuming no serious engine condition is found, a set of hotter plugs is the answer.

Normally plugs should look sort of brownish, or show a grayish tan, if the car is driven in the city and on the open road in fifty-fifty proportions. If driven mostly at low speeds the plugs would normally show white or yellowish deposits. Leaded gas causes this type deposit, too. Cleaning is sufficient here.

A final test of cleaned, properly gapped plugs, is to have them checked at a shop where they use a comparison tester. This puts your plugs against new ones and will save you trouble and disappointment if one or more plugs you have fussed with turns out to be an electrical dud. Use a torque wrench for the final installation of the old or the new set of plugs, following the car maker's recommendations carefully.

One good rule is that the smaller the plug size the less pull you need on the wrench handle. Guard against distortion of the plug shell which would adversely affect the electrodes' gap.

For a 10 mm plug 12 lbs.-ft. torque is about right. For a 14 mm plug pull to 25 lbs.-ft. For a 16 mm plug 35 lbs.-ft. is about right. This is for cast iron heads. For aluminum heads torque to 10, 22 and 25 lbs.-ft. respectively.

Let's Get Started

A motor must have a rich mixture, a hot spark and sufficient compression

MOTORISTS have been starting motors ever since Dobbin first stepped aside in favor of the internal combustion engine, yet there probably is nothing in driving that continues to be as baffling as the power plant that won't go into action. But regardless of appearances any such difficulty invariably can be traced to absence of one or more of the essentials for cold motor combustion.

Putting it briefly, the motor won't start if it lacks a rich mixture, a hot spark and sufficient compression. This sounds like a fairly simple combination to obtain, but since it is dependent upon a number of other factors the way to success with a cold start is immediately beset with obstacles. Let's take them one at a time. And especially let's be on the lookout for some of the things that can trip us up.

For example, we know that a cold engine needs to be choked so that its pistons can suck in a rich spray of liquid gasoline

since there is no heat to vaporize the fuel normally. But time and again there's delay in starting simply because the carburetor's bowl is dry. No matter how efficient the automatic choke the cylinders starve under such conditions. Fuel can be lost from the carburetor's float bowl by evaporation, by leakage into the intake or out of the carburetor, and sometimes by fuel creeping up the inside of the bowl by capillary attraction and then escaping around the gasket. Normally the fuel pump should be able to refill the bowl almost immediately as the starter spins the engine, but often the pump is weak and takes its time. Pretty good evidence of this sort of thing is when an engine will fire immediately, then stall and refuse to start until it has been cranked for a minute or two.

When the bowl is empty there is no advantage in pumping on the accelerator pedal. When there is this starvation, and if the car has been standing out in the cold

A WELL-TUNED ENGINE can be expected to start more easily regardless of the weather.

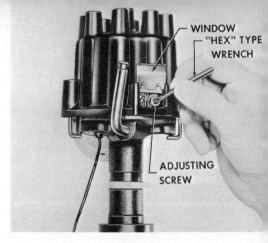

WINDOW
"HEX" TYPE
WRENCH

ADJUSTING
SCREW

NEW external adjusting distributors are an aid in keeping the ignition timing correct.

LIGHT OIL helps boost cranking speed and compression for much quicker starting.

for several days, it will help to disconnect the high tension wire that goes into the top of the distributor and crank until the carburetor has become refilled. Wipe any condensation off the tops of the spark plugs, the coil and the distributor cap, replace the high tension wire, check to see that the choke valve is fully closed, and then press the starter button. Failure to start after these precautions would be due either to weak spark or to low compression. Both such conditions can be due to the engine not having sufficiently light oil. It works out this way:

Congealed oil slows down cranking speed. That lowers compression. Since the battery is working overtime to crank the engine, voltage for ignition is greatly lowered. Ever since the introduction of the combination ignition and starter switch it has been impossible to crank and then quickly switch on ignition for a better start under adverse conditions, so we have little choice except to use light oil and keep the battery fully charged. One simple way to insure better starting is to fast idle the engine ten or fifteen minutes twice a week with the car outdoors. If this is done when the engine is cold the generator will charge at higher rate. However, if the car is given frequent runs on the open road the battery

should stay charged. Make sure the generator is in good condition and that battery posts and connectors are clean and tight.

With a normally rich mixture, a good spark and fast cranking to build up needed compression conditions are basically right for starting. But many detailed lapses can cause failure, or at least delays. One of these is need for cleaning and regapping the breaker points. Spark plugs that are fouled either because of a too rich mixture at all times, oil pumping past the piston rings, or because they are not a hot enough type for the engine or the way the car is normally used, will surely give trouble in starting. Often as the engine is cranked the battery weakens, thus lowering voltage for ignition. Best trick when caught with this condition is to stop and wait a half hour or so. Often after such a pause for recuperation of the battery the engine will start right off.

Ice in the fuel lines or the filter bowl will be a real headache. So will a water pump that is jammed with ice because the cooling system hasn't been sufficiently protected with antifreeze. Using jumper wires to an extra battery will be useless here. The car will need to be towed to a heated garage and the ice thawed out.

Much starting delay is due to trouble with the automatic choke. Often it is adjusted too lean. A common condition is an air leak in the tube which runs from the choke's thermostatic coil to a "stove" on the exhaust manifold. Moisture gets into the tube, forming ice. Even if weather is too warm for ice the moisture will cause corrosion which can be just as troublesome. Remedy here is to replace the heat control for the choke.

Whether to pump on the accelerator pedal for a quicker start is dependent on a

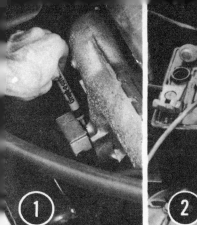
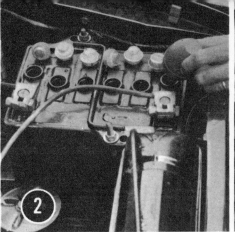
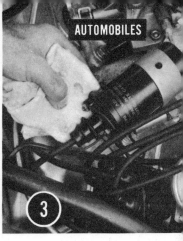

(1) SLOW warmup often due to manifold heat control valve sticking, doesn't preheat mixture. (2) Battery solution level kept low in cold weather. (3) Wipe parts to prevent "flashover."

number of conditions. If you can start the engine without pumping so much the better. However, it always helps to "crack" the throttle by pressing down all the way on the pedal and then allowing it to come back. Do this slowly. The effect of this is to actuate the throttle mechanism at the carburetor so as to set the throttle at fast idle. If the fast idle control is known not to be operating properly, hold your foot about one third the way down on the pedal. Assuming the engine is cranking fast enough, and if there is no response then give the accelerator pedal a jab. Try cranking again. Remember that it is always better to crank in short efforts, rather than to crank steadily. In all of this go carefully with that pumping because you do not want to flood the engine. If flooding is suspected you can usually smell raw gas from the exhaust.

Too often overlooked is the condition of the starting motor itself. How long is it since you removed the cover band and examined the commutator? Doubtless it needs cleaning. The starting motor may also need new brushes. Be sure to see that the hot wire from the battery is tight where it bolts to the starting motor. And if starting is always difficult with an older car perhaps the battery cable needs replacing.

Behind a lot of starting trouble are problems with the starter drive and its related parts. We have come a long way since the drive pinion was forced into engagement with the flywheel ring gear by means of a small foot lever which you pressed for the start. Manual action has long since been replaced with a variety of automatic controls. The pinion itself may be a Bendix (inertia) drive. Or it may be the overrunning clutch type. These are easily replaced when, and if, they develop trouble.

But for both "drives" there are special controls. If there's a pushbutton on the dash this operates a magnetic switch steel plunger which pushes a contact disc across two terminals to complete a circuit from the battery to the starting motor. Or the car may have an overrunning clutch arrangement wherein the magnetic switch not only closes the circuit to the starting motor but also provides a mechanical shift for the pinion.

Another system adds a vacuum switch which works in combination with the carburetor's throttle shaft to permit starting by pressing on the accelerator pedal. This, too, uses a relay and a solenoid to close the starting motor circuit. The popular combination instrument panel ignition and starting switch is merely a convenient way to speed up the cranking process. The point to bear in mind is that in all these systems the current passing through the starter control system—switch, relay, etc.—is merely one that triggers the heavier current which flows through the starting motor itself.

Due to the use of automatic transmissions, and the importance of not cranking while the system is in Drive, Low or Reverse there is now additional wiring for what is known as the "neutral switch." No starting action is possible unless the driver first moves the selector lever to Neutral. Sometimes there is corrosion enough to interrupt any of these circuits so if the starting system seems to be "dead" always repeat switching on the ignition, placing the selector lever in Neutral or, in the case of accelerator pedal starting, moving the pedal up and then down again. Where the end of the solenoid plunger is exposed, starting sometimes can be resumed by pushing the plunger in by hand. •

What, No Re-Start!

Engines are often harder to start after they've been warmed up

AFTER so many years of fighting the problem of starting the engine on a cold day, it comes as quite a shock to millions of drivers to find that modern engines may be more trouble starting after they have been warmed up. It just goes to show that if it isn't one thing it's another.

There are different kinds of restarting difficulties, with special reasons for each. Most common of these is that familiar delay when trying to get action from under the hood after having parked the car while on a short errand. The owner cranks and cranks, and nothing happens. He attracts the attention of someone who may suggest giving the car a push. As soon as the car is rolling, and he moves the selector lever into Drive, the engine goes into action as if nothing had happened. Why? Suspicion ranges all the way from some special kind of ignition trouble to belief in a jinx.

Actually the fuel mixture has simply be-

NEWEST device for preventing hot engine stall thins out the mixture.

HOT desert is no place to have the engine stall and refuse to start up.

"VARNISH" on pistons slows down cranking speed 'til engine cools.

come over-vaporized from engine heat during the brief parking period. If the owner had taken time for lunch the engine would have restarted without the slightest delay. He could have avoided trouble merely by holding his foot half way down on the accelerator pedal while cranking. If that failed, he would then crank with his foot all the way down. The object is to open the throttle wide so as to let in enough air to lean down the mixture. BUT he must be careful not to pump on the pedal. That would simply make the mixture richer. Naturally the tendency is to become disturbed and to start pumping nervously on the accelerator.

If the engine cranks slowly when you are trying to restart, that's a different story. This may indicate that there is "varnish" on the pistons, especially if the engine has seen a lot of service. This is a tough form of gummy deposit which causes seiz-

SIMPLEST of all the causes of difficult restarting is fever from low water level.

ing when heated. Under such conditions it is smart to try adding another errand to give the engine a chance to cool off a bit. It will then start up again without delay. Varnish can be removed to some extent with careful use of oil additives, but usually the pistons will have to be removed for washing in strong solvents.

Frequently the engine will be reluctant to start again after the driver has taken the car out of the garage and switched off the engine rather than allow it to fast idle while going back into the house. The difficulty here may be due to over-choking. The engine is loaded up with raw gasoline. Here again, however, the best remedy is to crank with the throttle wide open, being careful not to pump on the accelerator. If that doesn't do the trick, wait another fifteen minutes.

When an experienced driver restarts the engine, he always takes into account the nature of things at the time. If the engine has been fitted with new rings he will suspect that they may drag a bit when heated and he won't be too surprised if cranking is too slow for starting. He will thus try to avoid short periods of engine idleness until the rings wear in a bit. He will, of course, be suspicious that the engine is running a little too hot and will be careful to see that it has the right kind of oil. Heating always presents restarting delay. I recall a case where they used very light break-in oil after a motor overhaul. Because of a sudden heat wave, the oil temporarily was much too light for the weather. Instead of helping the engine run cool it actually encouraged overheating.

Sometimes the restarting delay follows a stall. That is usually a headache because invariably it happens in traffic when the emotional factors blind us to what we must do to get started again. The stalling may be due to overheating or to true vapor lock, and in that event it is well to try to get pushed over to the curb to let the engine

cool. Usually, however, the stall is due to a little dirt unseating the carburetor's needle valve, or to the fuel pump overfilling the carburetor's bowl. In either event the best remedy is to crank with the throttle wide open. Do this in spurts rather than to crank steadily. If the needle valve is unseated it can sometimes be brought back to normal by tapping the outside of the carburetor's bowl near the gasoline intake.

One of the newer troubles with very high compression is the "dieseling" effect when trying to restart an engine immediately after a hot stall. Because the engine is firing its own mixture it tends to run backward, thus slowing down cranking speed to a point where it will not run normally. Use of more powerful starting motors solves this. You can solve it by waiting a minute after a hot stall.

Suggested Improvement

An improvement is to switch the suction line of the distributor's vacuum advance from the carburetor throat body to the intake manifold. This provides greater advance of ignition during idling which, in turn, results in a cooler running engine. That means less chance of hot stalling—less trouble restarting.

Difficult restarting when the engine hasn't as yet warmed up may call for cleaning out the heat tube to the choke and the screen over the thermostatic control. Heat can't get to the control fast enough to open the choke wide. The mixture simply is too rich. Another very common difficulty in damp, cold weather is stalling from carburetor icing. Best remedy here is to let the engine fast idle with the car outdoors for a few minutes until the throttle warms up. Some gasoline is treated to prevent this sort of stalling.

The better the engine's condition the less it is likely to present restarting trouble. This is well illustrated in the case of a starting motor that has been serviced so that it operates at peak speed. Combined with a fully charged battery this means faster cranking, quicker overcoming of any conditions that may be working against you. It is interesting to note here that most of the drivers who face restarting problems are those who make so many short runs, with short stops between crankings. Not only does this increase the various obstacles but it also pulls down the battery, thus spoiling one's best chance of overcoming difficulty.

I might add that if the engine is hard to start cold it will also likely kick up a fuss about restarting when warmed up, simply because it needs servicing in a big way. •

What's That Noise?

IDEAL TIME to check for chassis noise is when the automobile is on a lift for greasing.

WE MAY complain about high costs, lack of performance or low gas mileage, but actually what gets us down more than anything else is an unexplained noise. Squeaks, rattles and vibration are just not our dish.

Most mechanics today are so busy working on actual repairs they haven't much time for trying to find out why the car rattles at 38 miles per hour over North Main Street. So it is pretty well up to the car owner himself to do some sleuthing. He will find, for instance, that most squealing when an engine is first started indicates need for applying a dressing to one of its belts that drive the fan, generator and power steering pump. Sometimes the belt edge is merely glazed and can be roughed up with the blade of a screwdriver when the motor is switched off. Don't use grease or wax on a noisy belt, and be sure that the drive pulleys are in line.

In checking for the causes of car noises always try the car under different con-ditions. If, for example, a noise changes tone when the car traverses different kinds of road paving it is not due to a gear condition but to the tires. Noises heard in the rear of the car in rainy weather often are due to slapping leaf springs. Water splashed up from the road acts as a temporary lubricant, encouraging loose leaves to slide. Always try the car with and without passengers when noises develop. Weight on the car's rear may change the action of the rear shock absorbers, causing the car to thump when it "bottoms." Added weight in the car will change the sound of the exhaust system by making the engine work harder. Much noise is due to the exhaust system hitting the frame. A loose tail pipe may strike the gas tank.

Many noises come in or vanish with change in car speed. Every engine has speeds at which periodic vibration is noticeable, and the smart thing is to avoid such speeds wherever possible. But try to determine whether the noise or vibration is increased by conditions in the chassis. Run the engine with the car standing still, or coast with the car in Neutral. A noise that may baffle but which is nothing to worry about is a loose fitting heat valve in the exhaust manifold. It will tighten up of its own accord in due course. That birdie under the hood may be due merely to a dry cam of the distributor shaft. Those clicking hydraulic valve lifters are often quite a problem. Keep the engine as clean as possible by changing oil often and using the high detergency type. Avoid overheating since that thins down the best of oil and, by lowering pressure, prevents the valve lifters from working normally.

That rattling in the steering gear may be front-wheel shimmy caused, in turn, by worn universal joints which at higher car speeds allow the propeller shaft to whip. It is typical of how vibration can travel around the car and build up some real trouble and expense. When an automatic transmission recently lost its oil and picked up a lot of water, it was found that a leak had developed between the oil cooler and the radiator which are combined as a unit. The shop had had three other cases that same week, and they were all due to vibration.

Increase Inspection

In addition to avoiding certain speeds at which the car obviously runs "rough" it is important to step up inspection. Had the owners of the cars with the transmission trouble made it a habit to take a look into the radiator every few days, they would have seen signs of oil in the water and could have forestalled the transmission breakdown. Those loose motor mounts may be the cause of the air cleaner setting up a racket during idling. A defective vibration damper at the front of the engine may be quite troublesome, and so will a damaged fan.

A third rule is to know more about the particular design of your car. Typical is the split propeller shaft found on some late model cars. In this arrangement the two shafts have a carrier support about half way between the transmission and the rear end. If one of the bolts holding this carrier loosens, the shafts will set up a chatter which the frame of the car will amplify. The same condition will develop if the rubber mounting for the split-shaft carrier becomes damaged from excessive road splash or oil. Sometimes the carrier develops both ills, thus compounding the vibration.

Most automatic transmissions "klunk" when put into Reverse, especially when backing out of the garage with both engine and gears cold. This is nothing to worry about. Something that calls for a change in driving habits, however, is a thud heard when starting away with some automatics and running about 10 miles per hour. This sometimes is due merely to failure to accelerate progressively. The driver hesitates and invites the thumping action. There are cases, however, where this is due to trouble with slip sleeve at the rear end of the propeller shaft. Hardened lube or burrs on the spline will cause a knocking sound even with cars with conventional drive.

You can often check vibration at the brakes by changing the rate of car speed decrease. If the brakes tend to squeal, and you are sure the brake shoes are properly adjusted, try increasing pressure on the brake pedal when you start stopping, then ease off toward the end instead of starting with a light pedal pressure and building it up toward the actual halt.

Right here we get into the realm of psychology. Don't be surprised if what appears to be evidence of trouble is just

LOOSE or badly adjusted brake shoes bring on variety of distracting, disturbing noises.

CENTRALIZED chassis lubrication systems are saving headaches from rattles, noises.

something fairly normal of which you are too conscious at the moment. It may be wind roar, or you may be too aware of the road surface. A lot of what passes for car trouble is due to exhaust vibration. Too light manifolds will set up a ringing noise; sometimes a drumming. So will a too light or too small muffler, especially when accelerating sharply.

An uneven adjustment of the brake shoes sets up localized high pressures, squeals and squeaks being the penalty. Glazed lining will have a similar effect as will an excess of drum dust or a loose backing plate. When the brakes set up a disturbing vibration one owner discovered that the front wheel bearings were loose. In a more involved case it was found that rivets touching the drum of one of the brakes set up harmonic vibration of the drum.

Brake chatter is another form of vibration with a long list of possible causes. You may face this some day if the brake shoe retractor springs are weak. Sometimes one of these springs is lost during careless service work or simply becomes detached.

When chatter developed in one recent case a mechanic found grease on the right rear brake lining. On another car there was excessive anchor clearance. In a case that was a little harder to crack an observing mechanic discovered that one of the drums was loose on its hub.

A groan or grunt is also evidence of vibration, but you'd never suspect that it can come from too tight wheel cylinders or a binding master cylinder. Dirty brake wheel cylinders will also have this effect.

That buzzing noise heard in a car with a torque converter is usually a sign that the system's oil level is low. Or either the front or rear pump in the transmission may not be working properly. A ringing noise in the converter is another type of vibration. It can also be a warning of low oil level. In one type converter mechanics look for a damaged suction pipe or a defective pressure regulator valve. Whistling in another automatic transmission traces back to trouble with the converter's control valve or with the drive sleeve of the front pump. •

NOISES come from (A) loose suspension arm (B) stones hitting low cross-member of frame (C) squeaking bushings (D) loose brake backing plate (E) droning in muffler, exhaust system.

What's Missing?

Locate that motor miss simply and systematically

THAT time-honored pest—the motor miss—need not be so baffling if you will remember to study it carefully in the light of some known facts about engine misbehavior. Go after the miss systematically and you can't miss.

Several close cousins to the miss, such as bucking, jerking and surging, continue to baffle the car owner and bedevil his repairman. While these oddities in engine action may seem to be cut from the same pattern, there's considerable difference when they are carefully considered. It is the ability to note such differences that serve best when trying to find the exact cause and an appropriate remedy. Clearcut misses in the engine's operation usually indicate trouble with the ignition, and if the miss is prolonged (especially when hill climbing) breaker points may need attention. Complicating your efforts to get to the root of trouble is the fact that what shows up as a simple miss at normal driving speeds may become a jerking action when speed is low, just as it would be when driving too slowly in high gear or if the ignition timing is too far advanced.

At lower speeds a simple miss will accent any wear on the universal joints, and may disturb the drive line to the point of introducing a pronounced jerking action. If the joints are not worn the engine miss may not be noticed when driving in traffic, but it will still be needlessly damaging to the drive line. An important point to remember is that under certain kinds of driving conditions missing will be much more noticeable.

Important, too, is the weather. An engine that tends to overheat may develop real trouble if it is forced into higher speeds on a hot day with the breezes behind the car. Here the cooling system is operating at a disadvantage. When the engine of his car started to miss during a snowstorm, one driver wisely suspected that snow flakes

were getting into the engine compartment to wet the ignition. He stopped the car for ten minutes, then proceeded at a slower pace. The same rule will often work in a driving rain.

Missing at higher speeds often is an indication that the spark plugs are not the right heat type. They are too hot. Even a plug that is cool enough for hard use may pre-ignite the fuel vapor if it is handicapped by being loose or if it was put into the engine with an old gasket. It is fairly easy to nail down the sort of miss that occurs when the car is accelerated, assuming there is no missing during idling. Here the plugs may merely be set for a too wide gap. Trouble with a plug or two will also cause a miss under such conditions.

Much trouble with today's engine is due to flashover of high tension current along the route to the plugs. This will result in bucking since one or two cylinders will be getting spark when it isn't wanted. For some unknown reason engine miss is seldom suspected as being the result of a weak battery, poor connections or faulty grounding.

If the usual checks for ignition trouble fail to provide a clue to motor misbehavior there's a good chance that the problem is one of poor valve action. Here it is necessary to be on your toes so far as observation goes. When one motorist found that the engine missed while idling but not when driving the car, he asked his mechanic to give the motor a vacuum test. Just as he suspected one of the valves was leaking. While pulling the car this valve was forced to close sufficiently to restore reasonably normal compression to the affected cylinder. Weak valve springs show up as missing at higher speeds because they are unable to close the valve quickly enough. A continuous miss from a faulty valve may be an indication that its spring is broken. Valve springs often "shimmy." And as for the valves themselves there is common stickage due to gummy deposits on the valve stems or in the guides. This will vary in degrees of engine misbehavior. If a valve stem is warped, the valve will likely hang up and produce a constant miss. Any valve with a warped head will produce a continuous miss, less noticeable as speed increases, simply because of the overlapping impulses of the pistons.

MISSING on hills is often corrected by replacing the points. On a long hill (photo at left) coil trouble or sticky valving may account for the motor miss.

DUSTY ROADS, like the one shown above, may result in dirt getting into the fuel system. To fight this, check the fuel filter; also check the air cleaner.

Any prolonged miss is easily confused with lack of fuel supply, but the tip-off to such lack is coughing (real backfiring) through the carburetor. If missing comes in after an abrupt slowdown, the chances are that either the carburetor float is disturbed or that oil has sucked up past the rings and fouled out a plug or two for an instant. A too lean mixture that causes a miss during idling, as well as during slow pick-up, may not be a handicap when the driver tramps on the accelerator. That is because the acceleration pump enriches the mixture and overcomes the effect of air that has leaked in around worn valve guides or leaky intake manifold gaskets.

Jerking and bucking when slowing down in high gear may call for a relocation of the suction tube for the distributor's vacuum control. Distributor advance mechanism is a common cause of engine roughness. When an engine surges or bucks with a closed throttle, at moderate speed, there may be a too rich mixture.

Keep in mind that there are more engine speeds than slow and fast, and idling. Acceleration from low speed as well as from road speed should be considered as two additional brackets. Then there are deceleration as well as what mechanics call "floating on the line." In the latter case the engine is loafing, the car floating along on its own momentum. In the lower speed bracket such floating is apt to develop into a surging action. In new cars this often is due to stiffness or to too little clearance between valve stems and guides.

Idling vagaries can be caused by too little tappet clearance, gummed up hydraulic valve lifters, a too advanced spark and failure of the vacuum spark control. In addition to the other matters which I mentioned earlier in this chapter also consider the possibility of a clogged low speed carburetor jet. A good rule to follow when trying to track down any such conditions is to accelerate the engine frequently when testing. This helps "normalize" it.

One owner discovered that a miss during acceleration was due to having drawn

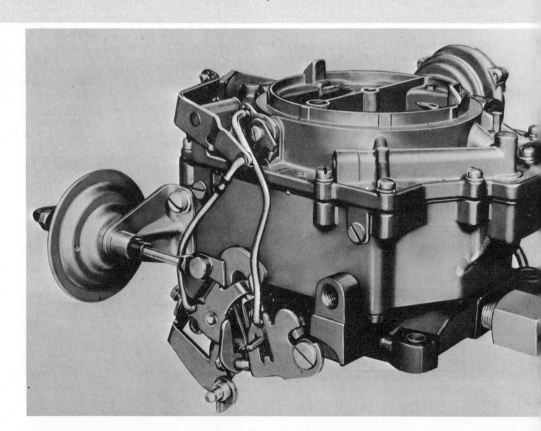

NEW TO many is the throttle return valve which checks stalling with automatic drives.

down too tightly the cover plate over the spark plugs. High tension current was jumping from the top of one of the plugs. Another series of misses which are apt to be overlooked stem from the engine running too hot. This brings on a tendency toward vapor lock—the condition in which fuel goes into vapor form in the lines to block its own flow. Improper venting of the gas tank may cause missing or surging at higher car speed. Camshaft trouble comes in on rare occasions. And, of course, weakness of the fuel pump is always a possibility.

The wandering miss is a special problem. Among causes not so likely to be considered are sticky pistons and spark advance irregularities. A dirty air cleaner can be the cause of a low speed miss, as will a too rich or a too lean mixture. Low compression or a weak coil may bring on missing at any engine speed. If the engine breaks into a series of misses at a top speed well below average the answer may be a weak breaker arm spring. •

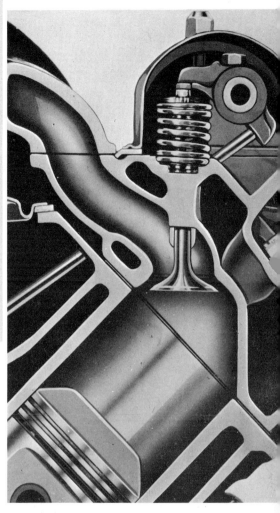

VALVE at the left has a damper to prevent surge and valve trouble at higher speeds.

FREQUENT pest is the sticking valve which puts one cylinder out of business, as shown.

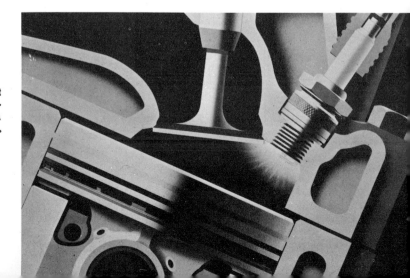

WEAK COIL may not lessen the spark's intensity, but will shorten the duration of spark.

SMALL BLOCK BARBECUE

It costs less than $10 to build,

will give years of satisfaction

By David X. Manners

HERE'S a barbecue you can build in three hours and which will give satisfaction and pleasure for many years. The cost is well under $10.

A foundation slab is important in a barbecue. It ties the entire structure together so that, like a boat, it can float undamaged over any ground swells caused by frost or earth movement. But you needn't do the heavy work of pouring a concrete foundation for this barbecue. Make a matte of reinforced brick instead.

On a firm, well-drained site, dig out an area measuring 38x40 inches to a depth of six inches. Level off the bottom of the excavation and tamp it well. Place bricks in a basket pattern—three this way, three that—to fill the area. Mix a mortar batch of one part mortar cement, three parts sand.

Then, after thoroughly blending the dry ingredients, add water until the mix has the consistency of mud. With your trowel, shovel the mortar between brick joints to half their depth.

Reinforcing Rod

Cut a 20-foot length of ½-inch reinforcing rod into six lengths measuring 40 inches each. The rod is readily cut with a hacksaw. Make cut halfway through, then break rod apart. Place a rod in each of the cracks that transverses the matte. Fill the cracks with mortar flush with the top.

On a bed of mortar, and two inches in from the rear of the base, place two masonry blocks to form the back of the barbecue, and a block to form each side. With bricks placed flat in a mortar bed, fill in between the blocks and make an apron

UNIT requires only 12 masonry blocks and 68 common bricks. Reinforcing rods serve as both the grate and the grill.

FILL CAVITIES of blocks with stones or rubble, or pack in crumpled newspaper within inch of top.

FINISH OFF top of blocks with mortar, leveled smooth, or crowned slightly at the center, as shown.

PUNCH HOLES at intervals in a 15½x15½-inch sheet of heavy metal. Fold over sheet edges.

INSERT SHEET into barbecue. It forms fire pan, rests on the grate bars which were installed earlier.

COMPLETED UNIT looks like this. Barbecue is easy to build, will give excellent service for many years, many barbecues.

in front of them. Lay bricks roman style, that is, with unbroken joints.

Cut six 27-inch lengths of ⅝-inch reinforcing rod. Place three of the rods across the barbecue as a grate before adding the second course of blocks. Atop the second course, add the remaining three bars to form the grill. Now add the third and final course.

Fill in the cavities of the blocks with rubble and mortar and finish smooth. In a 15½x15½-inch square of heavy sheet metal punch holes at two- to three-inch intervals. Edges of sheet may be bent double for reinforcement. Sheet metal pan is supported by grate—and barbecue is ready for use. •

MATERIALS NEEDED:

12 masonry blocks
68 bricks
6 rods ½x40 inches
6 rods ⅝x27 inches
1 bag mortar cement
2½ cu. ft. sand

HANDY ROD GRILLS can be placed on rods, will hold hamburgers, hot dogs, even large steaks.

EXCAVATE AREA measuring 38x40 inches to a depth of about six inches. Level and tamp the area.

PLACE DAMP, not wet, bricks on edge in basket-weave pattern—three this way and three that way.

FILL CRACKS to half depth with mortar, place three ½x40-inch reinforcing rods across matte each way.

FILL CRACKS to top with mortar and smooth. No need to wait for setting, go ahead with block work.

PLACE BLOCKS in bed of mortar, two blocks forming rear of unit, a block on each side. Check level.

FILL AREA between blocks and apron with bricks laid flat, joints unbroken. Set grate rods in place.

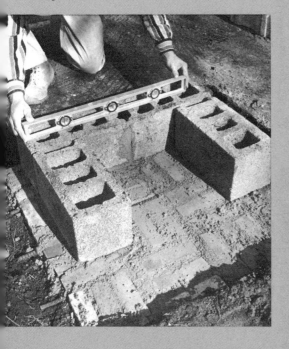

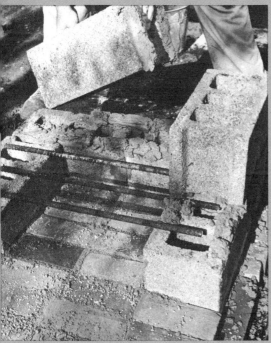

PLACE SECOND course of blocks, staggering joints. Cut block with brick, cold chisel for half blocks.

PLACE THREE ⅝x27-inch rods across the unit to make the grill, then add the top course of blocks.

BLOCK-AND-BRICK BARBECUE

This combination makes for easy construction and attractive appearance

By David X. Manners

IF YOU want to build a barbecue, but don't relish the effort involved, use block in its construction. Every block is the equivalent of about a dozen bricks. Straight block construction may not be as attractive as all-brick construction, but in combination with brick it is indeed practical and handsome. The 42 blocks used in the construction can readily be placed in a couple of hours. It would take more than a day to lay the 500 bricks that otherwise would be required.

Preferably, locate the barbecue so it faces in the direction of prevailing winds. You'll find it burns better, and that the draft will carry the smoke produced by ignited drippings away from the cooking area.

Drive in stakes to mark the four corners of the subbase (A), which measures 58x76 inches. Then string a line from stake to stake to outline the rectangle. Use a rafter square to make sure all corners of the rectangle are right angles. If you don't have a rafter square, measure the diagonals of the area you have laid out. They should be equal in length. If the diagonals are not equal, the layout is lopsided. True up the corners so that the diagonals are equal.

Dig out the area to a depth of 8 to 10 inches and backfill to within 3½ inches of the top with crushed rock, cinders or gravel. This provides good drainage under the slab and minimizes the chances of frost damage. With a tamper or garden roller, compact the fill and be sure it is level. Wetting down the fill will aid in compaction, and will also prevent the fill from sucking water from the concrete that's to be poured on it.

Form for Barbecue

Make a form for the concrete slab (B) out of 2x4's, using two nails at each corner. If you don't drive the nails all the way in, they'll be easier to pull out when you remove the form after the concrete has set. Brace the form now by driving in foot-long stakes along its perimeter. Inside measurement of the form should be 54x72 inches. Use a spirit level to make sure each of the four sides of the form is level. Then check the level across the form from side to side and from front to back.

Approximately 8 cubic feet of concrete will be needed for the 3½-inch slab. Make the concrete of 1 part cement, 2 parts sand and 4 parts gravel or crushed stone. In most areas you can get sand and gravel already mixed in proper proportion. Allowing for waste, you'll need approximately two sacks of cement ($1.50 per) and 12

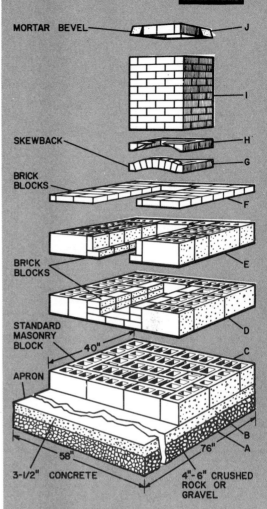

CUT MASONRY BLOCKS with a chisel, or chop apart with the edged end of bricklayer's hammer.

cubic feet of sand-and-gravel mix ($2.75 will buy a half yard). Mix dry ingredients thoroughly before adding water, and use no more than five gallons to a sack of cement. If you use Sakrete gravel mix for the job, you'll need about twelve of the 90-lb. sacks (about $1.25 per).

Pour the concrete, leveling it off even with the top of the form by using a straight-edged board. When the concrete has begun to set fairly stiff (probably an hour or two), use a wood float to smooth off the surface of apron to a final finish, but keep the slab under the barbecue proper rough. This will insure a good bond with the blocks above. Cure the slab by keeping it moist for at least 48 hours.

Building Barbecue

You can start on the barbecue structure as soon as the concrete is hard enough to bear weight. The mortar used in this construction is 1 part mortar cement and 3 parts sand. Thoroughly mix these two ingredients before adding just enough water to make a workable blend. A batch made by mixing three shovels of cement and nine of sand is the most you should mix at one time, for mortar should be used up within about half an hour after preparation. One sack of cement will provide enough mortar for laying 250 bricks, so you can figure on about 1½ sacks for the entire block-and-brick operation.

Experimentally, place the first course of blocks (C) dry to verify fit and arrangement, then remove the blocks, spread a ½-inch layer of mortar on the slab and set the blocks permanently. With a trowel, butter the wing ends of each block with mortar before setting it in place against its neighbor. Use the end of the trowel handle to tap the block level. A rafter square is handy for squaring corners.

The second course (D) of the barbecue includes solid masonry blocks, often called brick blocks. Used here as the ashpit base, they cover the voids of the blocks in the course below. If desired, fire brick or the same kind of face brick that is to be used for the chimney can be substituted.

Because bricks and brick blocks may vary in size, some trimming may be necessary to achieve the pattern shown. In construction of the barbecue as illustrated blocks adjacent to the ashpit lining were trimmed. Regular masonry blocks are readily cut with a chisel, brick-set, or with the edged end of a bricklayer's hammer. Cut or chop the block all the way around, but be careful of flying chips. Wearing of protective goggles may be advisable.

Compact the joints of each course as it is completed, using either a regular jointing tool, a piece of ¾-inch pipe, or a dowel. Compact the vertical joints, then the horizontal.

Brick blocks for the ashpit base are laid parallel to the front of the barbecue, and with unbroken joints. The sides of the pit are built up with two courses of brick blocks laid at right angles to the base. Mortar joints may be kept thin here, if required —$\frac{1}{16}$ inch being sufficient.

With this course (D) completed, begin placement of the next course (E). Note

IF CAPPING COURSE on base doesn't fit exactly, finish off attractively with mortar bevel, as shown.

FIRE IS BUILT on lower grate. Arch eliminates the need for a supporting lintel across the opening.

that the second of the two courses of brick for the ashpit walls is set on edge. As you proceed, constantly use the spirit level not only to verify that each course is level, but that the vertical faces are plumb. If you do not have a level, a straight-edged board may help in keeping block faces in line. A plumb bob or a weighted string will serve in determining vertical alignments.

Brick blocks are also used for the capping course (F). Place them as shown in the diagram. Do not worry about the blocks covering the area exactly. The rear edge, or the side edges, can be beveled with mortar. This capping course serves as a work area and a place on which to rest cooking equipment. The cooking grill rests on the cap's inside edges. The fire grate is the same size as the cooking grill (18x24 inches), but it is turned so that its short side is forward. It rests on the brick blocks forming the sides of the ashpit (D).

Dampen Bricks

A good quality face brick is desirable for the chimney, but common brick or even used brick will serve. Approximately 230 standard size brick are needed (4c each and up). Dampen the brick before laying them. Dry bricks will rob the mortar of its moisture and make it crumble.

The first chimney course (G) includes an arch. The arch, which adds distinction to the design, is simple to construct and is stronger than a metal lintel. It does, however, require a wooden support until it is set. Cut a board to correspond to the curve of the arch (a 20-inch radius), and prop it in place by any improvised means. Make the support easy to remove when the arch has set.

The seven bricks comprising the arch proper are all half bricks. Note the angle cut of the "skewback" bricks on either side of the arch. Cutting these bricks at an angle is important to the proper construction of the arch. Also note the trimming of bricks in the next course (H). This trimming, done with chisel or brick-set, levels off the construction thus far and puts everything back on an even keel.

Ten courses of brick (I) bring the chimney up to a proper level for the finishing course (J). Bricks in the finishing course are set on their side, rather than flat. This permits a mortar bevel, which is not only attractive, but also helps shed water and prevents moisture penetration of the brick joints below.

The top of the chimney should be at least at eye level, never below it. If you are well over six feet and plan to do the chefing, you may find it desirable to add an extra course or two of brick before placing the capping course.

Do not build a fire in the barbecue for two weeks. Break it in carefully then with a small fire that's kept burning for several hours. It's wise to repeat this break-in every spring. In the winter, metal parts are easily removable for storage. Always leave cooking grease on the grill until just before its next use. It keeps the grill from rusting between times.

Keep these pointers in mind as you build this barbecue.

LIST BELOW gives the materials needed to build barbecue. Use of masonry blocks saves time, effort.

CAP COURSE on chimney is made by setting the bricks on edge, then filling between with mortar.

MATERIALS NEEDED:

42 masonry blocks
90 block bricks
230 standard bricks
2 sacks mortar cement
5 cu. ft. sand
2 sacks portland cement
12 cu. ft. sand-gravel mix
2 18x24-inch grates

FIREPLACE UNIT (Albert Control-A-Grill) fits into barbecue in area shown in these two photographs.

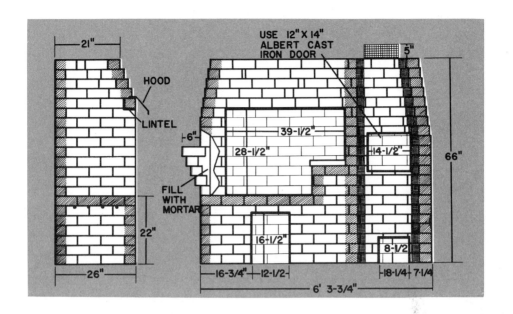

USE 12" X 14" ALBERT CAST IRON DOOR

DOUBLE-DUTY BARBECUE

It contains a brick barbecue and an incinerator in one compact unit

By Louis Hochman

CLEANING up after a paper-plate outdoor barbecue party is a cinch with this double-purpose brick barbecue which combines both a barbecue and an incinerator in one compact decorative unit. Designed and built by Outdoor Sales and Construction Co. of Sherman Oaks, Calif., the barbecue is made entirely of brick, both common and firebrick and will accommodate a 17½-inch wide Albert Control-A-Grill barbecue unit. One of the attractive features of the unit is its unique cooking chamber which is shaped like an inverted "L" to provide an 11-inch work shelf alongside and on a level with the

barbecue grill. This shelf is topped with 3½x11½x1½-inch red cap, and can also serve as a warming shelf to keep bread and other foods close to the warmth of the charcoal fire.

An inside 5¼-inch thick wall divides the unit into two separate chambers, allowing for the incinerator section on the right. This trash burning section should be lined with an inner wall of firebrick, to provide sufficient heat insulation. The grate for the incinerator is made by bridging a series of parallel ½-inch round 20-inch long steel rods across the outer and inner walls at a height approximately 12 inches from the

243

INCINERATOR in barbecue should be lined with inner wall of firebrick to provide sufficient heat insulation.

ground. The ends of these steel rods are embedded into the mortar between the brick courses.

Steel rods are also installed in a similar manner across the sixth course of bricks on the other side to support the firebox floor of the cooking chamber, as shown in diagram. Butter each brick well with mortar before laying it on the rod shelf so that it will bond to the rods and form a solid base.

The space under the cooking chamber serves as a storage bin for fuel and tools. Leave a 12½x16½-inch masonry opening as shown, to accommodate a 12x16 Albert Steel door. To the right of this door in the incinerator section, leave a masonry open-

ing of 8¼x10¼ inches for an 8x10 Albert Steel door. This is the cleanout section for removal of ashes from the incinerator.

The opening for the incinerator door should begin with the ninth course of bricks, and should measure 14½ inches wide by 12½ inches high. This opening will take a 12x14 cast iron Albert door.

To support the bricks across the top of the barbecue pit opening, mortar a 4-foot long, 4x4-inch angle iron, or lintel, across the 16th course of bricks as shown in diagram. The bricks can then be laid directly on this lintel to bridge the opening.

On the side of the structure near the barbecue, a small decorative brick shelf is built out as shown to serve either as a

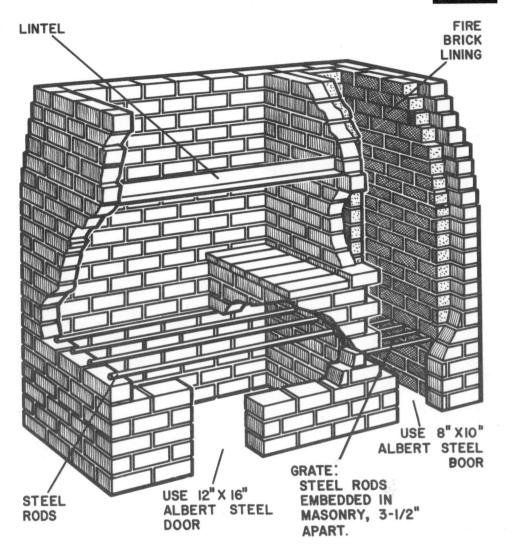

LINTEL

FIRE BRICK LINING

USE 8" X 10" ALBERT STEEL DOOR

STEEL RODS

USE 12" X 16" ALBERT STEEL DOOR

GRATE: STEEL RODS EMBEDDED IN MASONRY, 3-1/2" APART.

flower pot holder or as a place to lay the cooking utensils down while working. Make this by letting one of the brick in the ninth course jut out about 1 inch from the surface of the side wall. The brick directly above this one can jut out about an inch further, and the one above this can jut out its full 4-inch width. These staggered bricks form the bracket support for the final two bricks which are laid on them parallel to each other and at right angles to the wall, as shown. The gap left on the inside surface of the wall where the bricks jut out, should then be filled with mortar as the inner layer of bricks are added to for the double thickness side wall.

The top of the unit tapers slightly to angle the lines inward toward the chimney end. To achieve this effect, step the bricks inward toward the top, offsetting each course on the barbecue side about ¾ inch, and on the incinerator side about ½ inch. Start off-setting on the barbecue side with the 16th course, and on the incinerator side with the 14th course. The front should also be tapered inward at the top in the same manner, starting with the 18th course.

On the incinerator side, allow an 8x8½-inch chimney opening in the top and cover this with a 5-inch high box-shaped spark catcher made of 12 gauge, ½-inch wire mesh. Allow the finished barbecue to cure for two weeks, sprinkling it daily for the first week, before using it. •

245

SMOKE OVEN

It not only smoke-cooks food,
but also serves as
a barbecue and hot plate

By David X. Manners

FOR centuries the Chinese have practiced smoke oven cooking. Once you've sampled some, you'll understand why. Turkey, shrimp, hamburgers, oysters, duckling, steak, salmon, chops, spareribs, haddock, game, sturgeon, cheese—all have an indescribably delicious flavor when smoke cooked.

Food to be cooked is hung from hooks in the "chimney" where fragrant smoke collects from a hardwood fire built in the firechamber. A damper on the lid covering the chimney is regulated to control the fire and produce the degree of heat desired. An inexpensive oven thermometer hung in the chimney is an accurate temperature guide, but you can follow instinct, if you prefer.

Most meats cook best at about 300 degrees. For a rare steak, do a 3-inch cut for 20 to 30 minutes at 300. Hamburgers and hot dogs are cooked in 5 to 10 minutes at 300. Pork chops are ready after about 45 minutes at 350-degrees. Marinate food before cooking for varying taste.

Since the smoke oven is actually nothing but a barbecue with an oversize chimney, it's readily adaptable to conventional barbecue cooking. You merely remove the smoke lid from the chimney and replace the stove top with a grill.

The slab for the smoke oven measures 40x60 inches and is made by pouring a 1:2:4 concrete mix into a form made of 2x4's. This 3⅝-inch slab requires between five and six cubic feet of mix. You can save on concrete requirements by throwing in some large rocks, but be sure they don't project above the surface. Use a straight-edged board in leveling off the pour.

Trial Layout

You can begin building the oven itself the next day. First make a trial layout by placing bricks loosely in their approximate position. A grate that will do for your fire chamber can often be found at a junk yard at a fraction of the price new ones cost. It should be approximately 18x20 inches and fit loosely so it can be removed if replacement should at some future date become necessary. You can vary the size of the fire chamber to accommodate the grate you get.

The outside diameter of the 20-inch flue tile section, to be placed in the upper part of the chimney, measures 24 inches. Make a "compass" of two nails with a 12-inch length of connecting string and scribe a circle on the concrete where the chimney is to be centered. Around the circle, place

FOR OVEN'S BASE, make 40x60-inch form of 2x4's, level it, pour concrete, smooth off with form boards.

ON HARDENED BASE, make a "dry run" assembly of bricks, grate to allow for variation in brick size.

GUIDE LINE for chimney is made with string-and-nail in 12-inch radius. Lay bricks outside circle.

LAY BRICKS in ½-inch bed of 1 part mortar cement, 3 parts sand. Cut bricks in half with brickset.

FIRST TWO courses of chimney base are filled in solidly with bricks or rubble, then filled with mortar.

JOINTING TOOL compacts mortar, cuts away excess, smoothens. Use tool when mortar begins to set.

FOURTH COURSE has lining of full bricks set on edge. Removable pan sets in well for drippings.

half bricks in a ½-inch mortar bed. Mortar is made of 1 part mortar cement and 3 parts sand. Mix dry ingredients thoroughly and then add just enough water to give it the consistency of heavy mud. Butter the side of each brick with mortar before placing it alongside its neighbor, and tap it firmly into place.

Fill the inside of the chimney circle solidly with rubble for two courses, then plaster this base over smoothly with mortar.

Side walls of the fire chamber are built up three courses, with a 14-inch wide opening left in front for ashpit access. The grate is placed over the ashpit at the three-course level.

As brickwork progresses, "strike" the joints with a mason's jointing tool, or use a piece of pipe or rounded dowel. In striking, mortar in the joints is compressed and smoothed, the excess falling away.

When you reach the chimney's fourth course, lay a row of whole bricks on edge within the outside circle of half bricks. These edge-set bricks form the lower chimney lining. As on the outside circle, alternate joints of succeeding courses.

The firebox grate is placed about 7½ inches back from the front. Use steel angles to support the bricks that span the ashpit opening. You can buy new 1x1-inch angle stock, or you can pick up the metal rail of an old bed at the junk yard at fractional

FIRE CHAMBER GRATE may be bought new, or at junk yard. A 1x1x24-inch angle spans ashpit.

PLACE FULL BRICKS across ashpit opening, fill ends with bricks cut to size. Cut bricks on board.

TEMPORARILY SUPPORT bricks over opening. Be sure ends of bricks are well-buttered before placing.

SECOND ANGLE behind bricks spanning ashpit opening supports firebrick lining. Check level often.

cost. Use a hacksaw in cutting off two 24-inch lengths to span the opening.

Cut the two outside bricks down to 6 inches for the angle-supported course that spans this opening. This allows two full bricks in the middle, with one end of each firmly supported on the side walls. Place bricks to be cut on a board and rap sharply on the head of a broad-blade chisel with your hammer. Constantly use a spirit level to check the level and plumb of your work, and supplement its use with sighting by eye.

Place a second 1x1x24-inch angle across the ashpit opening behind the first course of bricks. This one supports the firebrick lining course. Two courses of firebrick

are placed at the front and two sides of the firebox. They are set on edge. The height of the chimney is now brought up to five courses to match the height of the firebox.

Using your brick trowel, plaster the inside of the chimney with ½ inch of mortar. The mortar covers all irregularities and makes the lining of the chimney smooth and unbroken.

With a third course of firebrick, set flat and overhanging the course below, the top opening of the fire chamber is narrowed down to accommodate a hot plate top. If you cannot salvage a top from an old coal stove at your junk dealer, a ¼-inch steel plate may be substituted, but the stove top arrangement is handier. The one used here

SWITCH FROM firebox to chimney building so that entire structure goes up at once. Grate fits loosely.

PLASTER INSIDE chimney with ½-inch coat of mortar. This covers irregularities, smoothes lining.

USE EITHER ½-inch rods or angles to support firebrick for firebox top. Lay firebrick with tight joints.

SPACE BETWEEN firebrick and brick facing is filled with mortar. Stove-lid assembly rests on firebricks.

is a two-lid section, but a four-lid section might be used to even better advantage. The stovetop is the place to prepare coffee and warm beans and other vittles to go with your smoke-cooked dinner.

A 26-inch support is needed on either side of the stovetop opening for holding the firebrick where they close in above the firebox. Use either angle stock or a ½-inch reinforcing rod. At stovetop level an 18-inch angle is needed for bridging the opening where chimney meets firebox.

Build the chimney to three courses above the stovetop, and complete plastering of the inside lining with mortar. A two-foot length of 20-inch (24-inch outside diameter) flue tile is now set in place.

Weight of the tile may be near 200 pounds, but you won't find it much of a chore to lift one side of it three or four inches at a time. The trick is to block the tile up on alternate sides with bricks, blocks, or what have you, until you have it at the level desired, then slide it over in position on the chimney. In lieu of this, call on a strong neighbor for help.

Continue the brick work around the tile until the top is reached. The chimney lid for the smoke oven is 24 inches in diameter and is made of ⅛-inch steel, reinforced with a ¾-inch edge band and cross bands on the underside. A four-inch hole cut in the lid is covered by a plate that swivels on a rivet. This is the damper. A handle

USE ANGLE to bridge opening where chimney abuts firebox top. Angle may be any scrap rail.

PLACE BRICKS atop bridge. The 11th course is last before placing flue tile. Complete interior plastering.

GET HELP to lift heavy flue tile in place, or block it up in easy stages until you reach desired height.

METAL LID sells for $12 at local forge. Place mortar cap on brickwork, allow ⅛-inch lid expansion.

on each side of the lid eases its removal. Cost of having such a lid made at your local forge or sheet metal shop will be about $12.

Set the metal lid in position atop the chimney and around it plaster a mortar cap covering the brickwork. Make the cap flush with the top of the lid and level it toward the outside. Jiggle the lid slightly when mortar begins to set so there'll be about ⅛-inch space between lid and mortar for possible expansion.

In use, meat is hung from hooks supported by ½-inch rods placed across the flue tile and under the lid. Tidbits, such as shrimp, are smoked in a suspended wire basket. Good eating! •

MATERIALS NEEDED:

450 common brick
18 firebrick
1 20-inch flue tile
2 1x1x24-inch angles
1 1x1x18-inch angle
20 feet ½-inch reinforcing rod
3 bags mortar cement, 9 cu. ft. sand, 5½ cu. ft. concrete
stove top, chimney lid, drip pan

MODERN STONE BARBECUE

This easy-to-build fireplace
makes a fine family project

By Ralph Mattison

YOUR first step in building this modern stone barbecue will be to determine the right location. Pick a spot accessible to the eating and relaxing area, secluded, and favorable to prevailing winds. It might be advisable to check your local building code regarding any possible restrictions.

The barbecue shown here was built just a few steps from a flagstone terrace bordering on an irregularly-shaped fish pond. The spot chosen was hilly, and the fireplace was set right into the hill.

Use the whole family to dig out the foundation area, as we did. That way they'll know they had a part in the building.

With the digging completed, make a form of wood boards 2x8 inches. The form should measure three feet wide, eight feet long. Be sure this form is absolutely level, and tampered down into the dirt. Then mix and pour concrete into this form to the full length of eight feet. This will give a foundation more than adequate for the purpose. For additional strength, you can put in a few iron reinforcing rods. Keep the footing wet and in the curing process for about a week.

The base, which contains storage and cooking areas, is red face brick. The spacious working areas on top of the storage compartments are blue stone slabs. The chimney is beautiful gray Crab Orchard

FIRST STEP is to choose location, mark it off with string, dig bed for concrete base. Be sure sides and floor are kept level.

WOODEN FORM is put in place. Since location is a hillside, slope was used to nestle rear of fireplace. Form must be level.

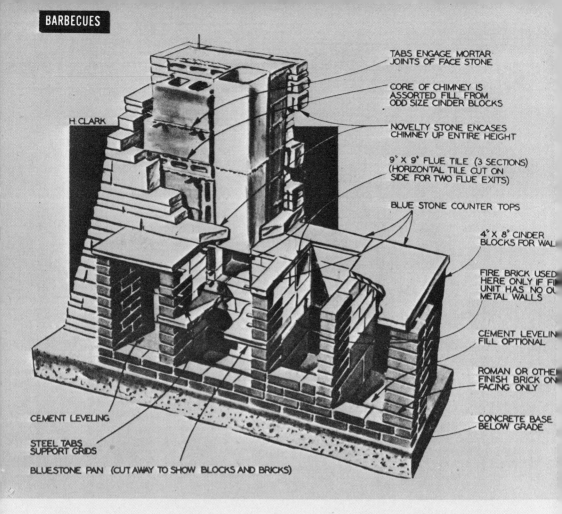

TABS ENGAGE MORTAR JOINTS OF FACE STONE

CORE OF CHIMNEY IS ASSORTED FILL FROM ODD SIZE CINDER BLOCKS

NOVELTY STONE ENCASES CHIMNEY UP ENTIRE HEIGHT

9" X 9" FLUE TILE (3 SECTIONS) (HORIZONTAL TILE CUT ON SIDE FOR TWO FLUE EXITS)

BLUE STONE COUNTER TOPS

4" X 8" CINDER BLOCKS FOR WAL[L]

FIRE BRICK USED HERE ONLY IF FI[RE] UNIT HAS NO O[R] METAL WALLS

CEMENT LEVELIN[G] FILL OPTIONAL

ROMAN OR OTHE[R] FINISH BRICK ON FACING ONLY

CONCRETE BASE BELOW GRADE

H. CLARK

CEMENT LEVELING

STEEL TABS SUPPORT GRIDS

BLUESTONE PAN (CUT AWAY TO SHOW BLOCKS AND BRICKS)

AFTER CONCRETE has "cured" for a week, begin to set up blocks at rear, and red facing brick, as shown. Before tying these permanently together with mortar, it's wise to see if pieces fit properly.

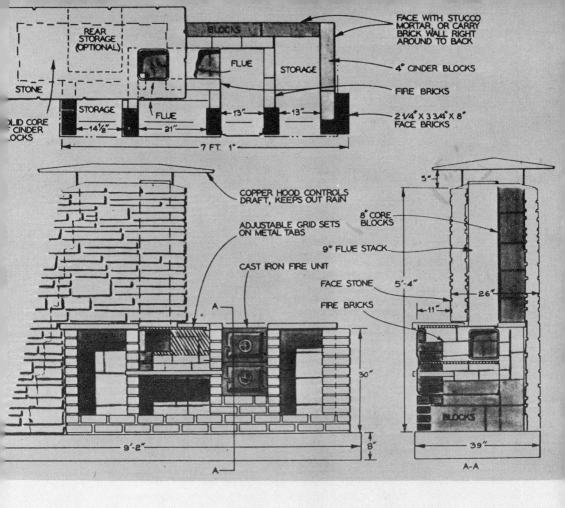

WHEN YOU are sure each unit of design fits into proper place, take away top bricks and apply mortar to lower layers. Then build up layer by layer as planned in your earlier game of "block building."

ON THE WAY toward completion, fireplace now has all basic unit-areas permanently defined. Before mortared joints are dry, however, check to be sure grills, shelves and firebox fit the areas allotted for them.

NEXT STAGE toward completion is building up the walls in front of barbecue, then the walls along the sides. Build both groups up to their full height. Do neat and careful job.

THIS PHOTO shows how bluestone shelf is placed. First lay bricks up to required height (4 bricks high over bottom 2-brick-layers) then place shelf and set permanently with mortar. Add four bricks on top.

TAKING SHAPE, fireplace now has flue and cinder block interior of chimney in place. Drawing on page 6 shows exact stage of construction at this point. Note cinder block in rear wall of the barbecue.

READY FOR the chimney facing of Crab Orchard stone, one work area of bluestone is now already set. The Crab Orchard stone will be built up around the cinder block and flue tiles.

CHIMNEY FACING is easy to place. Varying shapes and colors of stones offer many possibilities in design. As you progress in this work, you'll probably become fancier and fancier, do a spectacular job.

NEARING job's end, second bluestone work table is laid on right side of fireplace and along the right rear.

FINAL touch is the copper hood which serves to keep rain out of the cooking units, adds a handsome atmosphere.

COMPLETED fireplace sets well with surroundings of foliage in back yard. A few flagstones in front always help.

stone, which is built up around the cinder block and flue tiles. The design of this fireplace is so flexible that many other materials might easily be used.

The firebox is a ready-made unit, fitted with lift-out lids and grates. Manufactured by the Majestic Company, this unit has a regular grate in front. The rear section has a plate for frying.

When starting to build this barbecue, set your first layer of blocks, bricks, fireplace unit and grates into position atop your chosen footing area before pouring concrete. This precaution makes doubly certain that everything is going to fit.

After the concrete facing is laid, you can start building. Outside of your facing, around the fireplace unit and open grill, use fire brick. And don't forget to install hangers for the grates around the grill while laying the fire brick. It's very easy to forget this.

In laying and cutting the Crab Orchard stone you'll have a lot of fun and more than likely find yourself getting a bit fancy toward the top, doing things you wouldn't have dreamed of when you began. The stone lends itself nicely to abstract design as photos here show. •

MATERIALS NEEDED:

24 8x8x16-inch cinder blocks

60 4x8x16-inch cinder blocks
    for chimney, back and side of base

3 sections 8x8x24-inch flue tiles for
    chimney

50 2x4x8-inch red face bricks for base

50 2x4x8-inch fire bricks
    for use around cooking units

25 corrugated wall ties for securing
    Crab Orchard stone to cinder block

9 bags Portland cement
    footing, base and chimney

1 ton Crab Orchard stone chimney facing

1 yard sand   1 yard gravel

1 Majestic fireplace unit

2 Majestic grates

8 hangers for grates in open grill

1 sheet copper, angle iron, bolts and bolt
    sticks for hood

Planning Your Basement

Your cellar can become the most attractive and functional area of your home with the proper planning and a little know-how.

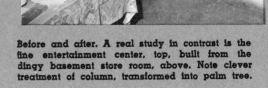

Before and after. A real study in contrast is the fine entertainment center, top, built from the dingy basement store room, above. Note clever treatment of column, transformed into palm tree.

THE best bargain in living space is obtained by transforming your basement into a bright and clean family room—with plenty of space left over for laundry, workshop and other special purposes.

Today, new materials and techniques have solved most cellar problems: oil and gas burners eliminate dusty, smelly coal bins; fluorescent lamps bring daylight into the darkest corners; mastic adhesive and plastic tiles seal out concrete floor dust and moisture; acoustical ceilings drown out noise; vapor-barrier sheeting and other materials block moisture penetration; plastic furniture upholstery ends mildew nuisance; dehumidifiers and ventilator fans purify the air, while new heaters keep even the basement floor pleasantly warm.

Actually, only a nominal expenditure will make a basement usable—but you could go all the way to indulge your fancy and wind up with a fancy downstairs nightclub.

The cost of the work should not be regarded as an expense but rather as an investment increasing the value of your home. Banks recognize basement finishing as a home improvement qualifying for a government-backed loan. Local real estate agents will confirm that a finished basement makes a home more salable and valuable.

Of course, it would be impossible to give data on every single detail; but there's no need to repeat the instructions that are supplied by manufacturers of particular products, which you can obtain in the form of free booklets and pamphlets. In fact, an effort is made here to steer you to needed information of this type by references to various instruction pamphlets that can be obtained free for the asking. But where fundamental information is important—such as step-by-step process of framing the basement walls—the subject is treated with as much detail as required on the assumption that you're a beginner. Where possible, technical terms are avoided, but sometimes it is essential for clarity to resort to a basic nomenclature which will become self-explanatory.

Living in Style

Give your basement a lift by making it the kind of room you've dreamed about. Plan it on a specific overall theme that appeals to you and meets your special interests.

You may like the flavor of an old-time ice cream parlor; this is easily worked out

Basement converted into comfortable living area utilizes a colored photo mural to give feeling of spaciousness. The dropped ceiling at left hides plumbing traps and valves.

Top left. Basement-living room has pine planking, cork tiles. Wall unit contains TV set, hi-fi speaker and components. Recess in wall holds study desk.

Above right. Original rock wall was retained to give textured feeling to attractive downstairs game room. Gaps in wall were filled with mortar.

Rugs can be kept on basement floor, left, if a suitable asphalt or vinyl-asbestos floor is laid. Simulated fireplace lends warm atmosphere to room.

BASEMENT PLAYROOM
16 FEET X 20 FEET, 7-FOOT CEILING

	Wall Framing Studs	Floor Tiles and Adhesive	Ceiling Furring	Ceiling Tiles	Wall Panels	Nails, Trim, Paint, Etc.
LOWEST COST ($200 to $300)	400 ft. (2x3) $35.00	320 sq. ft. Asphalt tile (dark) $35.00	340 ft. (1x2) $15.00	320 sq. ft. (hardboard or gypsum) $30.00	500 sq. ft. (Knotty pine finish in gypsum or hardboard) $40.00	$20.00
MEDIUM COST ($300 to $500)	400 ft. (2x3) $40.00	320 sq. ft. Asphalt tile (light colors) $50.00	340 ft. (1x2) $15.00	320 sq. ft. (fiber tile) $40.00	500 sq. ft. (20¢ grade, plywood, Weldtex, Surfwood, planks, knotty pine) $100.00	$25.00
BEST FINISHING (Over $500)	400 ft. (2x3) $50.00	320 sq. ft. Vinyl asbestos $100.00	340 ft. (1x3) $17.00	320 sq. ft. (acoustical tiles) $53.00	500 sq. ft. (40¢ grade plywood, Plankweld, Marlite, etc.) $200.00	$30.00

if you can dig up a number of swivel-type stools, and perhaps you can even locate a marble soda fountain discarded by a drugstore. Add a long wall mirror behind this counter with rows of sundae glasses on shelves to help the idea along.

If you're a tropical fish hobbyist, plan the wall framing for built-in fish tanks with small fluorescent lamps behind the walls to light up the showpieces. Filters and other accessories can be placed in cabinets behind the walls.

Perhaps the tropical South Seas is your cup of tea. A bit of bamboo trim around the windows and a palm tree (perfect cover-up for an unsightly column) will do the trick. Maybe you have some mementoes of your war-time service like Hawaiian leis to carry the idea further.

Most popular is the knotty pine room which gives you cozy beauty and serviceability at lowest cost. A complete chapter in this book will steer you right in framing, installing and finishing the knotty pine.

Making the Most of Your Space

The first question will be how to get all you want into the available space since, of course, the basement isn't unlimited in size. Right at the start, you'll have to compromise and forego some of the embellishments pictured in the slick magazines. But don't despair—there are ways to slide in an extra or two that will keep everyone happy.

For instance, you know the family wants a Ping-pong table and Junior must have a large enough place for his railroading outfit. Both take up lots of room so it looks like someone will have to be disappointed. But it's possible to get both into the same place—and use the large Ping-pong table for other purposes as well.

Similarly, you'll learn how to fit a real workshop—power tools and all—into a tiny corner if need be.

Planning the Project

The basement project must be carefully planned to avoid costly mistakes and to make the most of your space.

Largest open area should be allotted to the family playroom. This should be located for easy accessibility, preferably at the foot of the stairs, and with at least one window in the room. If there are lally col-

Schedule for Basement Finishing

1. Prepare the cellar. Correct any leaks, remove pipe obstructions, partitions, coal bins, shelves, etc.
2. Make floor plan sketch.
3. Put up wall studs, frame partition wall.
4. Ceiling furring.
5. Install electric wiring and fixtures.
6. Put up wall panels.
7. Frame out doorways.
8. Finish ceiling.
9. Install built-ins.
10. Lay floor tile.
11. Fit molding trim.
12. Hang doors, finish window openings, etc.

Wiring	Light Fixtures	Doors and Trim	Stair Treads	Decorations	Total Cost
Wiring and boxes $20.00	Incandescent (4) $40.00	—	Rubber pads $10.00	—	$245.00
Wiring, boxes and switches $25.00	Fluorescent (4) $60.00	Flush doors (2) $30.00	Tile or linoleum $30.00	—	$415.00
Wiring, boxes and switches $50.00	Fluorescent (6) $100.00	Flush doors (2) $35.00	Linoleum moldings $30.00	Window cornices, column covers, built-ins. $50.00	$710.00

Bamboo bar in a tropical room (see floor plan below) adds the final touch to a complete hobby and entertainment center. Walls are pine paneled, chairs for bar are homemade of reinforced bamboo sticks.

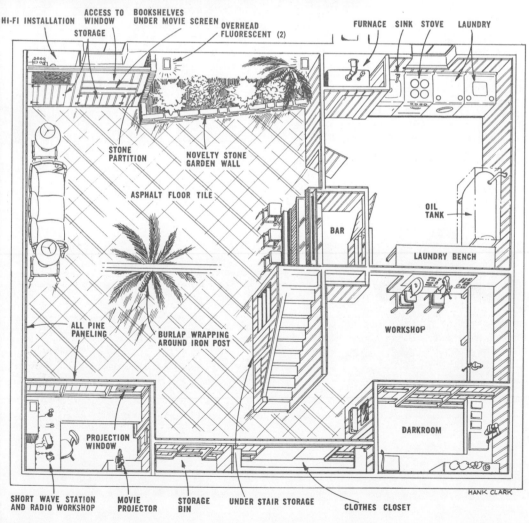

HI-FI INSTALLATION

ACCESS TO WINDOW

BOOKSHELVES UNDER MOVIE SCREEN

STORAGE

OVERHEAD FLUORESCENT (2)

FURNACE   SINK   STOVE   LAUNDRY

STONE PARTITION

NOVELTY STONE GARDEN WALL

ASPHALT FLOOR TILE

OIL TANK

BAR

LAUNDRY BENCH

ALL PINE PANELING

BURLAP WRAPPING AROUND IRON POST

WORKSHOP

PROJECTION WINDOW

DARKROOM

SHORT WAVE STATION AND RADIO WORKSHOP

MOVIE PROJECTOR

STORAGE BIN

UNDER STAIR STORAGE

CLOTHES CLOSET

HANK CLARK

264

Built-in wall units and bookcases help to conserve space. Lower unit houses audio system, records.

Canvas awning lends gay note to snack counter. Awning also hides fluorescent strips over shelves.

Elegant downstairs living room has gold-tinted wall panels, comfortable modern couches. Note how columns have been utilized as part of planter-box dividers. Floor has contrasting color square tiles.

For the teen set, music corner in basement helps to organize gay parties, dancing, jam sessions.

Early American feeling is emphasized by stucco wall and bracing. Ceiling beams were left "raw."

Decorative setting is achieved with wrought iron furniture, pine partition wall. Rug lends warmth.

Knotty pine built-ins form a complete wall of this youngster's cellar study and entertainment center.

umns, plan the room so a partition wall will include the column, or at least so the column is close to one side wall for minimum interference with parties, dancing or games.

The rest of the space then is distributed for laundry (with at least one window), workshop, and whatever special closed area you need, i.e., a guest room, ham radio shack, dark room, etc. The amount of space available will determine the treatment and arrangement. If you have a large ranch home, with staircases near the center, there will be plenty of space to have a playroom on one side and still have enough area on the other side for your special requirements.

A two-story house will have a smaller basement, which means that the playroom

Facilities for all family interests can be incorporated into a downstairs living area without requiring additional space. This movie screen rolls up behind the ceiling valance atop a built-in bookcase wall.

will take up most of the main section, leaving perhaps a 10-foot area along one wall.

Best way to start is to go right down and measure the floor area, making a rough sketch to scale size (1″ or 2″ equaling 1′) on a sheet of paper. Then you can arrange the rooms and get an idea of the proportions.

Spreading the Budget

Usually the biggest cost in construction work is labor, but the basement project is one that you can do yourself at leisure. This is especially true because there are no structural factors—walls, floor, ceiling and staircase are already there—all you will do is put on a finishing surface. You won't be hindered by weather conditions; you're not confronted with a time dead-

floor tiles for immediate use. You only pay for the materials.

What's more, it will be rewarding ex-line. You may prefer to do the job slowly and painstakingly in every detail or just slap up some wallboard and put down the perience that will develop your manual skills. It's a project, too, in which all the family can participate, even the youngest members.

Buying Materials

Even though you decide to keep the project at lowest cost, don't skimp on quality materials. For example, make sure that the 2x3s for wall framing are uniform, seasoned and straight. You'll save considerably on labor, and there won't be those irritating warped stud problems. ●

Wall and Ceiling Framing

FOR best results, concrete walls should be framed with studs to provide a nailing surface for wall panels, and to give an air space between the panels and foundation wall; the studs also serve as a base for anchoring electrical switches and junction boxes.

Studs should be of 2x3 lumber, of good quality so they will line up straight and true and thus make the entire wall project easier. It won't be necessary to use the heavier 2x4s since no structural support is required, except where a partition wall would need the extra strength of 2x4 framing.

In addition to the studs you will need 1x3 pieces for ceiling and floor plates to which the studs are nailed. Lumber for plates can be of any convenient length, but preferably 12 or 14 feet.

Don't use green, warped or irregular "bargain" lumber because the success of your entire project depends on sound framing.

The question is often raised as to whether 1x2 furring strips attached directly to the walls will serve as well as the more expensive 2x3s. There are several objections to the use of furring on cellar walls, chief of which is the fact that concrete foundations are rarely straight and plumb and require considerable shimming. In addition there must be a good deal of slow going masonry drilling to anchor the furring. Also, the thin furring does not offer a recess of sufficient depth behind the wall for installing standard electric boxes. Furring, in addition, makes it difficult to frame out around heating and water pipes and other obstructions.

Follow this procedure, which will be used throughout for wall and partition framing: start along one foundation wall. Nail a 1x3 across the ceiling joists, close to the foundation wall. If the joists run parallel to the wall, then you will have to bridge the space between the nearest joist and the wall sill; this is done with scrap pieces of 2x3s forced into the space, one every three or four feet. An easier way is to nail pieces of 1x3 under the joist, toenailed to the sill on the other side. The 1x3 will not interfere with the ceiling finish, as it is just the thickness of the furring that will be used later. When nailing the top plate to the joists, leave a space

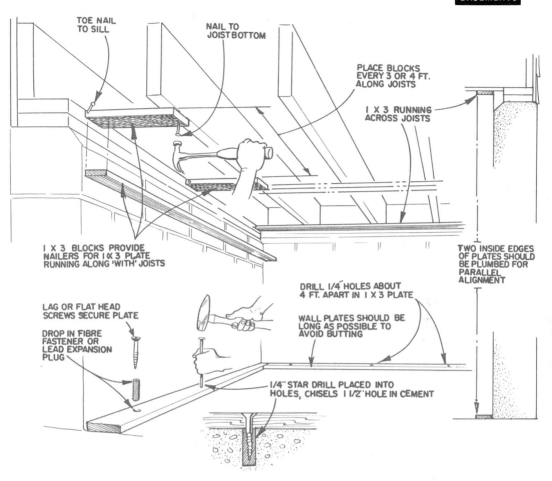

TOE NAIL TO SILL

NAIL TO JOIST BOTTOM

PLACE BLOCKS EVERY 3 OR 4 FT. ALONG JOISTS

1 X 3 RUNNING ACROSS JOISTS

1 X 3 BLOCKS PROVIDE NAILERS FOR 1 X 3 PLATE RUNNING ALONG 'WITH' JOISTS

TWO INSIDE EDGES OF PLATES SHOULD BE PLUMBED FOR PARALLEL ALIGNMENT

DRILL 1/4" HOLES ABOUT 4 FT. APART IN 1 X 3 PLATE

LAG OR FLAT HEAD SCREWS SECURE PLATE

DROP IN FIBRE FASTENER OR LEAD EXPANSION PLUG

WALL PLATES SHOULD BE LONG AS POSSIBLE TO AVOID BUTTING

1/4" STAR DRILL PLACED INTO HOLES, CHISELS 1 1/2" HOLE IN CEMENT

Floor plates must be fastened to the concrete basement floor. For best results use a masonry drill, ¼-inch, fot No. 20 Rawlplugs, lead or fiber anchors. Top of anchor can be leveled with floor using a special tools, as shown in photo below right. Make certain that the anchor is locked solidly into the concrete floor.

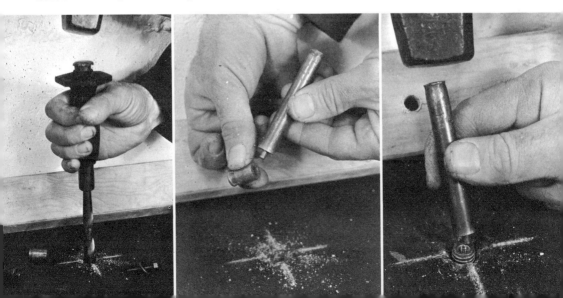

Screws attach the floor and ceiling plates. Always use plumb line to make certain that they line up.

Measuring stick, 4 or 5 feet long, used in conjunction with ruler, allows you to find stud length.

of at least ¾ inch toward the room so the ends of the 1x2 ceiling furring can be nailed on.

After the top 1x3 plate is nailed across or parallel to the joists, place a second plate in the same position on the floor. This must be aligned with the top one so that studs fitted between the top and bottom plates will be plumb. Drop a plumb line over the *front* edge of the ceiling plate and mark the position of the plumb bob on the floor. Do this every six feet to place the floor plate accurately.

The floor plate must be anchored to the concrete floor, at least sufficiently so the wall won't move when someone leans against it. Quickest way is to drive steel cut nails into the concrete through this 1x3, but some floors are so hard the nails won't go in. In that case, drill ¼-inch holes, about 1½ inches deep, for fiberplug or lead masonry fasteners, and attach the plate with screws into the plugs.

Saw each vertical stud to size separately, as you will want them to fit tightly between top and bottom plates for maximum support of the wall.

Start at a corner, where two studs are put up at right angles to each other so they provide a nailing surface for the wall panels from both directions. Best way to do this is to nail down pieces of scrap 2x3 to both top and bottom plates at the very corner. The studs will be supported against these corners while you toenail them in place. Make sure the stud backings are aligned plumb so the studs also will be plumb.

Now stop for a question: what kind of wall finish are you planning? If it is to be gypsum board, four feet wide, you will need studs 16 inches apart "on centers" which will give three vertical nailing surfaces for each panel; if the wall is to be knotty pine boards the studs may be 24 or even 36 inches apart, with several horizontal members between studs to give a nailing surface.

Now back to your corner studs. It is obvious that the first studs must not be 16 inches apart on center, as the wall panel will cover the entire end stud. So this first stud is an exception. The second stud thus is placed so that it is 15 inches away less only half the thickness of the 2x3—(about ¾ inch depending on actual measurement of your stock).

From there on to the end of the wall use the 16-inch O/C measurement. At the end put up corner studs as before, even if they are closer than 16 inches.

For knotty pine and similar walls, studs may be placed up to four feet apart but

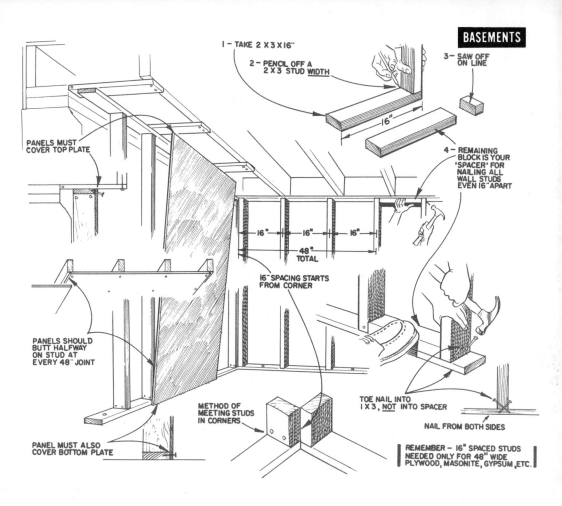

1 – TAKE 2 X 3 X 16"

2 – PENCIL OFF A 2 X 3 STUD WIDTH

3 – SAW OFF ON LINE

16"

4 – REMAINING BLOCK IS YOUR 'SPACER' FOR NAILING ALL WALL STUDS EVEN 16" APART

PANELS MUST COVER TOP PLATE

16"   16"   16"

48" TOTAL

16" SPACING STARTS FROM CORNER

PANELS SHOULD BUTT HALFWAY ON STUD AT EVERY 48" JOINT

METHOD OF MEETING STUDS IN CORNERS

TOE NAIL INTO 1 X 3, NOT INTO SPACER

NAIL FROM BOTH SIDES

PANEL MUST ALSO COVER BOTTOM PLATE

REMEMBER – 16" SPACED STUDS NEEDED ONLY FOR 48" WIDE PLYWOOD, MASONITE, GYPSUM, ETC.

Cut your stud to length to fit snugly between floor and ceiling plates; use a spirit level to check straightness. Studs are toenailed into plates by supporting one end with block of wood, as shown.

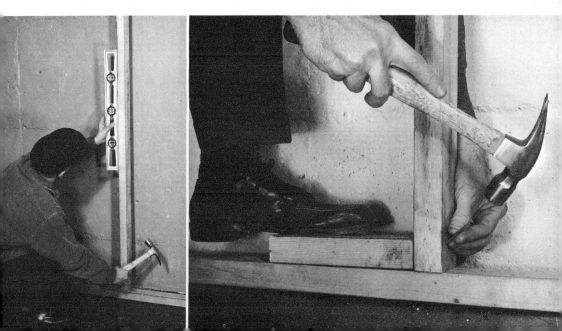

Cross members are alternated in height to enable you to nail their ends right through the upright.

Ceiling frames, 2x2 or 2x3 stock, are attached to joists. Drop ceiling to allow for pipes, etc.

are braced with horizontal members nailed solidly between studs. First get the studs well tied in, then cut the crosspieces to fit snug between them and nail in through the studs into the horizontal ends. Where necessary, toenail in from the sides. It is quite all right to stagger the height of these crosspieces so that you can nail into their ends from different levels. Attach your horizontals two feet apart.

Toenailing is the easiest method to fasten the studs to the top and bottom plates. The spacer will help you do this as it prevents movement on one side while the stud is anchored. It takes a bit of practice to drive the nails in easily without undue shifting of the stud, but you'll catch on soon enough. Drive at least two nails in each end, using nails of sufficient length to hold solidly.

An important point to remember is to check your work with a spirit level as you go. This is essential when putting up wall panels; if any stud is out of plumb the plywood edge may fall outside the nailing area and cause difficulty.

Studs also must be checked for straightness; otherwise the wall may bulge out. If the wall is to be finished with gypsum board, any distortion of the frame will cause the wallboard to "pop" by pulling through the nailheads.

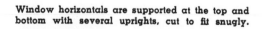

At windows, studs are sawed to fit in a frame around the opening, allowing sufficient clearance.

Window horizontals are supported at the top and bottom with several uprights, cut to fit snugly.

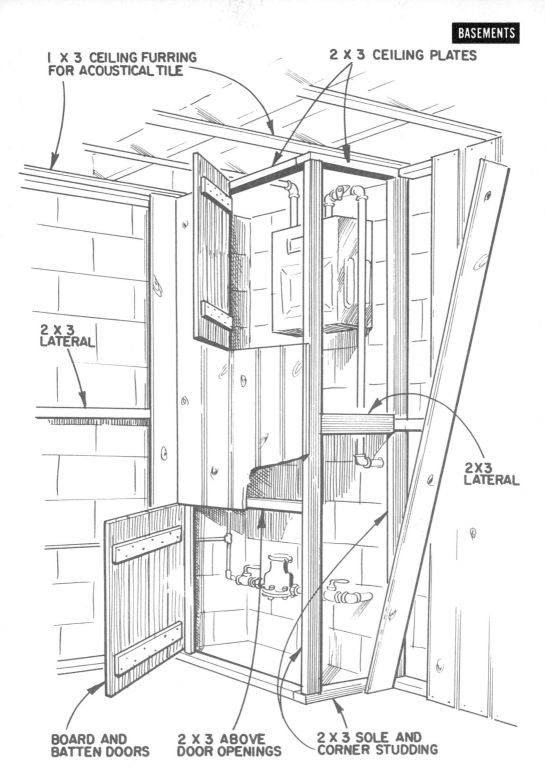

1 X 3 CEILING FURRING FOR ACOUSTICAL TILE

2 X 3 CEILING PLATES

2 X 3 LATERAL

2 X 3 LATERAL

BOARD AND BATTEN DOORS

2 X 3 ABOVE DOOR OPENINGS

2 X 3 SOLE AND CORNER STUDDING

TYPICAL FRAMING AROUND METERS — UTILITY BOXES — ETC.

Insulating batts, shown at right of photo, may be packed between walls to provide better warmth.

Keep a continuous careful check on plumb and alignment of studs as you work along the wall.

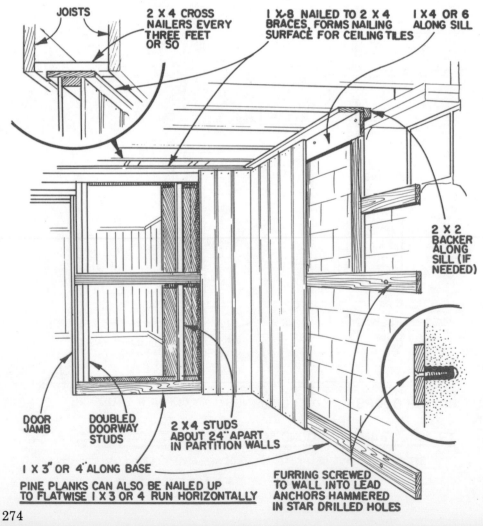

JOISTS

2 X 4 CROSS NAILERS EVERY THREE FEET OR SO

1 X 8 NAILED TO 2 X 4 BRACES, FORMS NAILING SURFACE FOR CEILING TILES

1 X 4 OR 6 ALONG SILL

2 X 2 BACKER ALONG SILL (IF NEEDED)

DOOR JAMB

DOUBLED DOORWAY STUDS

2 X 4 STUDS ABOUT 24" APART IN PARTITION WALLS

1 X 3" OR 4" ALONG BASE

PINE PLANKS CAN ALSO BE NAILED UP TO FLATWISE 1 X 3 OR 4 RUN HORIZONTALLY

FURRING SCREWED TO WALL INTO LEAD ANCHORS HAMMERED IN STAR DRILLED HOLES

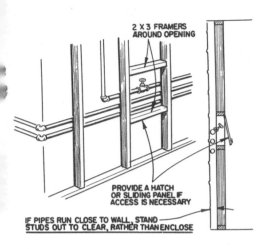

2 X 3 FRAMERS
AROUND OPENING

PROVIDE A HATCH
OR SLIDING PANEL IF
ACCESS IS NECESSARY

IF PIPES RUN CLOSE TO WALL, STAND
STUDS OUT TO CLEAR, RATHER THAN ENCLOSE

The most important part of plasterboard wall finishing is for the basic frame to be absolutely true and straight. Check your frame by holding a long straight-edge board against a row of studs. If one seems to be out of line, best thing is to reset or replace it right away.

You'll come across specific problems as you go, such as exposed heating and plumbing pipes, hot air ducts, windows, doorways, columns, steel girders and various obstructions. All must be framed around so the wall can be continuous.

Doors. Provisions for doorways must be made in the basic framework. Decide beforehand how wide the door will be. For most purposes, doors are 30 inches wide. Entrances to built-in wardrobes can be of the double flush door sliding type which may vary from 4 to 6 feet in width. Cedar closets, however, should be of only 24 or 30-inch width for better air sealing. Workshop doors can be standard 30 or 36-inch

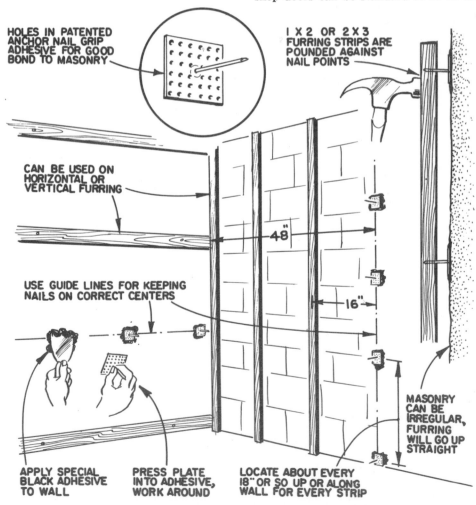

HOLES IN PATENTED
ANCHOR NAIL GRIP
ADHESIVE FOR GOOD
BOND TO MASONRY

1 X 2 OR 2 X 3
FURRING STRIPS ARE
POUNDED AGAINST
NAIL POINTS

CAN BE USED ON
HORIZONTAL OR
VERTICAL FURRING

48"

16"

USE GUIDE LINES FOR KEEPING
NAILS ON CORRECT CENTERS

MASONRY
CAN BE
IRREGULAR,
FURRING
WILL GO UP
STRAIGHT

APPLY SPECIAL
BLACK ADHESIVE
TO WALL

PRESS PLATE
INTO ADHESIVE,
WORK AROUND

LOCATE ABOUT EVERY
18" OR SO UP OR ALONG
WALL FOR EVERY STRIP

Frame around all meters, fuse boxes and valves.
Insert horizontals to support the short uprights.

Pipes and Valves. Where pipes run along the ceiling or near an end wall, use shorter studs to get around them if you can. In cases where water pipes and valves are along a wall, it may be best to build out the frame sufficient to clear the pipes, leaving a greater space at the back.

Some type of access door should be provided later for these valves. When a water pipe is located so that it seriously interferes with the framing, try to relocate it along a wall. This work usually is not very expensive in proportion to the value of usable space gained.

Utility meters and main shut-off valves must, of course, be left clear for emergency access. But you can frame around them if there is some means for access, such as a sliding door. Remember, also, electric splice boxes must not be lost in the wall but should be covered only with movable plates or doors.

Furring Out the Ceiling

Whatever type of ceiling finish you intend to use, you'll need uniformly spaced furring strips across the joists to provide a level nailing surface for the tiles or panels.

Before the furring is put up, nail in the ceiling light fixtures. These are just "roughed in" without the covers, so that furring may be placed all around the fixture boxes. The electric cables that will be drawn to the fixtures later are about the thickness of the furring and won't interfere with the ceiling tiles.

Furring consists of 1x2 wood strips. You can use the lowest-cost, rough-sawed grade, making sure they are fairly straight to minimize waste.

Nail the strips up at 12-inch intervals across the joists, making certain they are level. If there is any variation in the joist thicknesses, use pieces of wood as shims. Furring is placed along end walls, completely around all ceiling projections, light fixtures, along girders—in fact at every point where the ceiling tiles will end so that the edge may be adequately nailed.

Posts and Columns

Often the appearance of a carefully designed and finished playroom is marred by posts and lally columns. This need not be so, as there are ways not only to disguise the nature of the column, but actually to make them serve as part of the decorations. If you desire a large open space in the playroom, plan it in such a way that the columns become part of a partition wall at the end of the general playroom area. •

size, but you may prefer to allow for double 30-inch doors which will make it easier to roll tools in and out when needed.

Doorway openings should be at least six inches wider than the door itself to allow for two additional reinforcing studs and for the inside door trim. In construction, mark both sides of the oversize door opening on the floor plate. Saw the plate and place studs at the sawed-away ends.

Continue with the stud framing, 16 inches away from the door frame. You don't have to allow extra here for wallboard nailing as the door trim molding will cover it.

Windows. Frame studs around windows in this manner: place a last stud on the near side of the window, then cut the next stud shorter to go under the opening, and continue with a full-length stud on the other side. A horizontal header is then nailed over the shorter stud.

When framing a window allow at least several inches clearance at each side for finishing purposes, so that shutter doors, valance or other decorative trim will not cover the actual window area. This also will help give the impression of larger-size windows.

To allow space for a doorway, just cut the floor plate at that spot. Leave an opening wide enough to accommodate door and frame. Install a stud at each side of opening flush with cut off plate.

Wall Paneling

WHEN the framing, the ceiling furring and the electrical work have been completed, you can go ahead with putting up the walls; ceiling and floor tiles are installed afterward. Furniture can be built in before walls are finished, if desired, so that desks, shelves, etc., go deep into the stud framing. Generally, though, it is better to put up wall panels first, so there is a uniform backing behind the built-ins in the event of later changes.

Wall techniques vary according to the kind of material and can be divided into classifications based on the type of panels used.

Knotty Pine or Planks: These are tongue-and-groove boards of various widths nailed vertically or horizontally to the frame.

Large Wallboard Panels. Including gypsum board, fiber board, plywood, wood-chip board, hardboard.

Planks or Squares. These may be plywood or plastic-coated panels designed for invisible fastening to the studs.

Coated Walls. Any non-rigid material such as plastic or cork tiles, wallpaper, etc., which needs panel backing.

Paneling with Pine

Knotty pine boards come in various widths, with tongue-and-groove edging

Pine boards are nailed by starting at the corner of one wall. Face-nail into top and bottom plate. Blindnail sides through tongues with 1" nails.

First board must line up plumb against corner stud. Use a spirit level to check. Nail this board with its grooved side against the corner post.

simplifying installation by helping to lock the boards together into an integral wall surface. The boards are milled with an ornamental design along the edge; there is a different pattern on each side of the board so that you can choose either one for your playroom wall. Make sure, though, that you keep this pattern uniform, which-ever side you use.

An important consideration in paneling is the dimensional stability of the wood, which expands and contracts with changes in temperature and moisture content. So first, see that you get boards that have been properly dried or "cured" at the mill. You can be certain of this if your boards are produced by a member of the Western Pine Association, which sets industry standards for grading and drying.

In addition it is necessary to condition the lumber to the atmospheric condition in your home to prevent possible gaps and warping later. The best way is to stack the boards right in the basement room for about ten days. To assure good air circu-lation, place short sticks across the end of each board when you stack them up. Do this before you start the wall framing so that the boards will be properly condi-tioned by the time you are ready to use them.

The wood you select will have a bearing

Drive nail into board partway with a hammer, then use a nailset to avoid damaging the soft pine.

Install second board, aligning tongue and groove along entire length. Use scrap pine to drive home.

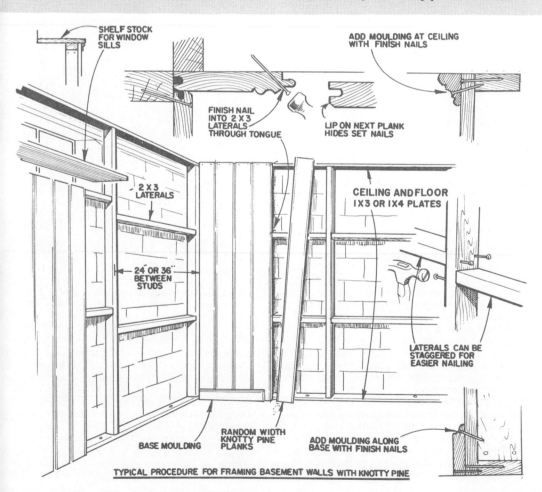

SHELF STOCK FOR WINDOW SILLS

ADD MOULDING AT CEILING WITH FINISH NAILS

FINISH NAIL INTO 2 X 3 LATERALS THROUGH TONGUE

LIP ON NEXT PLANK HIDES SET NAILS

2 X 3 LATERALS

CEILING AND FLOOR 1 X 3 OR 1 X 4 PLATES

24" OR 36" BETWEEN STUDS

LATERALS CAN BE STAGGERED FOR EASIER NAILING

BASE MOULDING

RANDOM WIDTH KNOTTY PINE PLANKS

ADD MOULDING ALONG BASE WITH FINISH NAILS

TYPICAL PROCEDURE FOR FRAMING BASEMENT WALLS WITH KNOTTY PINE

Panels may be cut full floor-to-ceiling length or they can be supported on 2x3 horizontal strips.

With both types of installation a contrasting base molding is used, held by 1" finishing nails.

Pine panels can be adapted for complete wall-length built-in units at the time of installation.

on the effect of the final finish. Light woods—ponderosa pine, Idaho white pine and sugar pine—are all nearly white and lend themselves to any treatment. When finished naturally, they remain light and the grain shows beautifully. A richer, darker feeling can be achieved with inland red cedar or incense cedar. White fir and Englemann spruce are other excellent light woods, while intermediate tones are best achieved with larch, lodgepole pine and Douglas fir.

After the boards have air dried at room temperature, they are cut to approximate lengths and "back primed." This consists of treating the surface that will be against the outside foundation wall to prevent mold or rot.

Formerly, paint was used for back priming but recently developed water-repellent compounds are less expensive and easier to apply. These are commercial preparations containing pentachlorophenol (commonly known as "penta"), available at most paint and hardware dealers.

Pre-finishing

While you could nail up the boards at this stage and do the finishing later, it is highly recommended by the Western Pine Association that the boards be finished first. This makes the job much easier, eliminates the possibility of streaks left by running paint and raw corners where the brush won't reach after the paneling is in place. All parts, including baseboards and molding, should be pre-finished. Refer to

Savannah oak planks, above, in random widths make for rich-looking walls, attractive colors.

Planks, left, are grooved along edges for easy installation with metal clips in special furring.

Below, sliding panels are used to gain access to valves or meters, become part of wall decor.

the following chapter for detailed information on pre-finishing the pine boards.

Nailing won't spoil the finish—knotty pine boards are put up by "blind-nailing" through the tongues and thus the nailheads are never visible. Nails at top and bottom are covered with crown and base molding.

Nailing up Pine Paneling

Boards should be cut to a length so they fit easily into the space without crowding; you can allow a bit of clearance at the top, which will be covered.

For vertical paneling, the first board goes up in a corner with its grooved edge into the corner. To see that it is plumb check with a spirit level, moving the board as required away from the corner stud. Any open space will be covered with the corner board that butts against it, or trimmed, if necessary, with quarter-round molding.

This first board is face-nailed at top and bottom. Use brads or thin finishing nails, 1½ inches long. Several nails may be fastened at the corner edge into the stud, then finishing nails are put through the tongue of the board into each horizontal frame.

A little practice will make you an expert at tongue nailing. Pine takes the nails well without splitting. Just hold the nail at an angle so that it will pass through to the 2x3 frame. Use a nailset to drive the nail in tightly, with head slightly countersunk.

The next board is lined up with the first, and the tongue-and-groove joints brought up snug, but not too tightly, leaving some room for expansion. If you have difficulty pulling the joints together, put the groove edge of a scrap piece of pine over the board and tap with a hammer.

Once you get started, the boards go up very quickly. At windows and other obstructions, just continue the pine facing over the frame by sawing the boards to length. At wall ends and other places where full boards widths will not fit, you might be able to use narrower boards with the same profile pattern, or simply rip the ones you have down to required width.

Wallboard Installation

Wallboard panels, in four-foot widths and of a length reaching floor to ceiling, are nailed to 16-inch O/C wall framing. Gypsum board and similar panels are surface nailed with the nails slightly counterset below the surface so that the heads can be covered with special putty or plastic spackle.

One type of gypsum board comes with a pre-finished surface that simulates knotty pine; for this type use enamel-coated nails which will be quite invisible because of the pattern.

Some plywood panels come with V-groove notches which add an attractive plank effect. The grooves are so spaced that they match the positions of the studs and nailheads can be recessed into the grooves and touched up with wood filler, colored to match the wood stain. Textured plywood and hardboard, Surfwood and Weldtex (U. S. Plywood Corp.) or Seadrift (Masonite), also permit invisible nailing.

Gypsum Panels

Gypsum board should be purchased to nearest required size for easier handling and less waste. You can make an allowance in length for the part later covered by baseboard and ceiling crown molding.

For example, if your ceiling height is 7 feet 2 inches, you can still use the 7-foot lengths rather than the 8-foot size. The panels will be blocked up from the bottom with 1x2 strips and later covered with the base shoe molding.

The panels are held tightly against the stud while nailing—don't depend on the nail to pull the panel close as you would with a wood surface. Use large-head blued nails, except on finished-surface sheetrock. Fitting need not be exact, as any small spaces or cracks between joints can be filled with spackle; but don't try to force an oversize panel into a too narrow space. The plaster board can't be compressed and may crumble at that point. Better cut somewhat undersize so the panel goes in easily.

Cutting, however, is simple and quick. Use a sharp wallboard knife, cutting against a straight-edge guide. Cut through one paper side of the panel, then turn over and snap along the scored line.

Panels must be nailed down tightly and securely, with nails spaced only about four inches apart on all studs and along top and bottom frame plates. If any misalignment in a stud forms a depression in the panel, don't expect to nail the panel down so it will stay; rather, replace the stud or build it out level with the adjacent ones by means of 1x2-inch boards nailed along the sides of the warped or poorly aligned stud.

If the wallboard panels are to be painted or covered with wallpaper, they must be taped and spackled at the joints, and nailheads covered smoothly with special cement and tape sold for this purpose.

Additional details on gypsum board installation are included in a folder on Sheetrock and Perf-A-Tape and may be

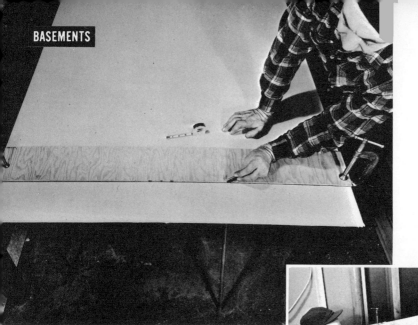

Sheetrock is cut quickly to size by running a sharp wallboard knife or razor blade along some straight-edge board; cut through surface covering.

After cutting through the surface bend panel down to split along scored line. Panel now hangs on its back covering. Do not break completely.

obtained by writing to United States Gypsum Co., 300 W. Adams Street, Chicago 6.

Plywood Paneling

Plywood panels, used in lightweight ¼-inch thickness to span across three studs, go up very quickly. Panels under 8-foot length usually are lower in cost, but in some cases, only standard 4x8-foot size panels are available—a waste of four square feet per panel if your ceiling is only seven feet high. Usually, you can use those narrow scrap strips for various purposes such as window trim, molding around built-ins, etc.

Panels may be nailed or applied with contact bond cement. The important point to remember is to put up the panels straight. If the first panel goes up plumb, the rest will line up correctly. But if the panels are not straight, it will be very noticeable because of the wood grain.

Inside corners can be butted together. or with one board overlapping the other. Outside corners can be treated nicely by chamfering the exposed edges so that they meet in a very thin line. Another method is to use special corner molding, usually of chromed metal, into which both panel edges will fit. Some plywood manufacturers supply moldings with wood veneered faces to match the panels.

Fir or textured plywood is put up with finishing nails. Prefinished plywood panels, however, can be glued to the studs to avoid use of disfiguring nails. Contact-bond cement is widely used for this purpose as no clamping pressure is needed.

Nail with small-head brads, countersinking the heads so the nail holes can be filled with wood paste or crack filler. For best results, brush some wood glue on the studs or furring behind the panels.

Contact bond cement is a practical applicator for plywood without nails. The rubber-type cement, adhering immediately

Right, holes for receptacles, etc., are easily cut with keyhole saw through drill holes in corner.

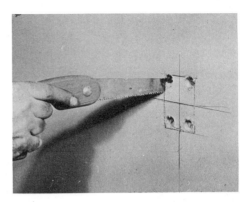

Below, after bending panel down cut through the back covering with a knife to separate the board.

Below right, if panel fits too tightly remove some of the edge with sandpaper to avoid damage.

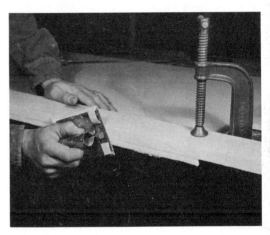

on contact, is applied in spots on both the studs and panels along the stud lines. The cement must dry thoroughly (about half an hour) before the panels are put up.

Pre-finished V-joint hardwood-veneered plywood is a recent development which is of great value for your basement project. The plywood panel surface is scored with V-shaped lines that simulate random width planking. These grooves are located to fall at the stud positions, so the panels can be invisibly nailed with small-head brads or finishing nails into the grooves. Nailheads are counterset and the holes filled with wood putty which has been stained to match the wood finish.

Planks and Squares

Plywood and plastic-coated Marlite planks come in $\frac{1}{4}$-inch or $\frac{5}{16}$-inch thicknesses and $16\frac{1}{4}$-inch widths with ingenious fastening devices. If the wall is first covered with gypsum board, which is recom-mended, the planks are applied with mastic adhesive spread over the panel, plus metal clips which fit into grooves in the sides. Each new plank covers the clips that hold the adjacent one, so the fastening is completely invisible. The clip-fastener system may be used also without wall backing, by just nailing to the studs, but the thin planks will lack the solid feel of an adequate backing and will have a hollow ring when tapped.

Squares in 12x12 inches, 16x16 inches, and other sizes, are applied over horizontal furring strips. The furring, of 1x2 stock, is nailed across the studs at required spacing. Squares of striated plywood, Weldtex, may be nailed directly over studs, but some backing is preferable to give support at all edges. Some squares, like plastic-coated Marlite, have tongue-and-groove joints for interlocking at all sides, but even so a wall backing is recommended. •

Finishing Knotty Pine

Care and preparation in finishing your wall panels will pay many dividends in the appearance and durability of your prize project.

FINISHING your pine paneling is one of the most interesting and rewarding steps of a basement or attic project. The variety of effects that can be achieved is almost endless; if done with care you can expect beautiful results.

The development of exciting new finishes is, in fact, partly responsible for the up-surge in popularity of pine paneling. The new finishes which run the gamut of color combinations glorify nature's infinite variety in graining and are a far cry from the varnish, stains or linseed oil finishes that once were standard practice.

A dark basement room should, of course, be treated with a lighter color scheme than a room with more natural light from larger windows. Remember, also, that pine, like all woods, tends to darken with age, so it's a good idea to keep the finish color light.

The basic requirement for successful finishing is smoothness, which you get with sanding—and more sanding. Good quality pine boards come factory sanded, usually on both sides, but a final light sanding before the finish is applied will remove the fine fibers that rise on the surface. Each piece should be carefully examined; rough spots, knots and pitch pockets thoroughly sanded. With pine, natural marks in the wood surface, like pitch pockets and knots, when properly treated can become decorative assets.

Sanding is done either by hand or with an electric sander. If done by hand, use a sanding block (a piece of one-inch thick wood) to hold the paper flat. Paper held down with the fingers will cause ridges in the wood which, however slight, will show up when the wood is stained.

The only electric sander you should use is the oscillating or orbital movement type.

Belt sanders work more quickly, but they are unnecessary because your knotty pine boards come pre-sanded and need merely a final smoothing. Belt sanders are recommended only for use on boards that are rough or dented. Disk sanders tend to gouge the wood and show circular distortion of the grain pattern.

The sandpaper for pine boards should be 0 or 2/0 grade. For a final smoothing, to get a perfect surface, use 6/0 or 7/0 paper. A recently developed paper of carbide grits will be helpful because the paper lasts indefinitely and can be washed to restore its effectiveness after use.

To get down to the actual job, let's take a favorite finish and carry out its application step by step. White-limey, for example, is highly popular and lends itself to a variety of final wall effects. It is modern in feeling, light in color, yet provides a good background for any decor. It is a good choice if you want to make a bright room out of a poorly lighted basement.

The first step is to mix your paint. For white-limey you take flat white lead and mix with turpentine or commercial paint thinner until it is of priming coat consistency. Then add a small amount of lamp black so that the mixture is just a little off-white. The mixture should be thin enough so it can easily be applied and wiped off, but not so thin that you will get a washed-out effect. Instead of lamp black, other color pigments such as blue or red will give you a novel and interesting hue.

When you are satisfied with the tone and thickness of your paint, do a bit of experimenting. Take several fair-sized pieces of waste wood, the same as the paneling you are going to finish. On one piece brush on a coat of paint, then take a lint-free cloth and just wipe off the knots. On the second, apply paint and quickly wipe the whole board. On another piece of wood allow the paint to stay on for ten minutes, then wipe completely. After 24 hours, when all these samples are dry, select the one that is closest to the tone you want for your walls and use the procedure you followed on that particular sample for the paneling.

If you are not satisfied with any of the samples, adjust the color by adding white lead to make the white stronger, or by adding thinner to tone down the effect and allow more of the natural grain and texture of the wood to show. Make a note of the proportions used in mixing the ingredients so that, if you run short in the middle of the job, you can match the original.

Having mixed and tested the paint, you are ready to apply it to the panels. To make the task as easy as possible, place four boards, face side up and several inches apart, over a pair of sawhorses. Now, standing on one side of this bridge-like arrangement, brush on the paint with long even strokes, *always* in the direction of the grain.

Sand boards before finishing. Use fine grade paper to get a smooth and even panel surface.

Mix primer for desired color to get limed finish. Brush on first coat, allow to set for 10 minutes.

Before paint becomes too stiff wipe off with soft cloth, leaving desired amount of whiting on.

Allow paint to dry thoroughly and rub with fine steel wool, then apply coat of brushing lacquer.

Remember to stir your paint now and then to assure uniform consistency. If you notice that the solvent is being absorbed by the wood, but that the pigment looks weak on the panels, it is probably because the mixture is too thin. In this case, add more pigment.

Be sure to apply paint also to the tongue-and-grooves of the boards so that if, after installation, the paneling adjusts to changes in humidity, there will be no visible streaks of unfinished wood.

After wiping for limed effect, let the paint dry for 24 hours. Then sand lightly with number 0 sandpaper. You now are ready to apply the protective surface coatings which are of shellac, clear varnish or brushing lacquer. If you prefer an antique effect, simply apply two or three coats of wax over the paint. Several top coats are desirable, each coat thoroughly rubbed with fine steel wool.

Popular variations of the white-limey are a blonde finish and driftwood gray. If you want the blonde finish, the only difference in the procedure already described would be in letting the paint stay on the wood ten to twenty minutes before wiping.

There are numerous little tricks used to highlight the warmth of the wood and to accentuate the interest value of irregularities in the panels. One of these is to take steel wool and lightly buff the knots and the grain in the center of each panel after wiping the paint or stain.

Another is to dust powder color over the natural tiny pockets around the knots. For example, the use of gold or aluminum dust will produce a rich glitter which will highlight the knot. Even bright reds and blues, dusted in deftly, will accent the knots with an eye-catching brilliance.

For a driftwood finish, coat each panel with a dull green stain which is at once wiped off. When this has dried, the panel is painted with neutral gray that is wiped off more thoroughly at the edges than in the center. This gives an uneven gradation, with the green showing through more noticeably at the edge than in the center. The grain of the wood is clearly visible.

Many interesting finishing recipes can be drawn from comprehensive color folders published by the Western Pine Association. One folder describes a silver beige called Tuolumne Tawn. To achieve it you simply brush on liberal amounts of aluminum (silver) paint, then wipe off immediately, allow to dry and apply clear finish.

For free copies of the color finishing folders write to Western Pines Association, Yeon Building, Portland, Oregon. Mention the finishes in which you are interested.

Furniture Finishing

Unpainted furniture sold by lumber dealers and department stores is in great favor because the well-designed cabinets, desks and chests are practical and adaptable to many interesting combinations that can even be joined into a complete wall unit. The pieces are usually made of clear Ponderosa pine or hardwood, and the cost is often quite close to what you would have to pay for the lumber itself if you were to make your own project.

You can get amazingly beautiful finishes, rivaling that of expensive hardwood furniture, with a little practice and attention to details by following the directions given here.

Remember that this furniture is not suited for a "clear" finish—shellac or unpigmented lacquer—because many of the pieces are built of solid lumber consisting of glued-up board widths.

Each piece of wood has varying color tones, grain appearance and fiber density,

Final finishing with shellac or lacquer can be postponed until all the boards are nailed up.

After last lacquer coat is dry, the wall may be given a slight gloss by polishing with hard wax.

so that clear stain or shellac will accentuate the different graining and appearance of the jointed boards. The usual method of applying penetrating stain produces the same result and thus is also objectionable.

For best results with your unfinished furniture follow the steps that are given here for staining and finishing in a light birch color. This procedure can be adapted for any color tone you may want.

First, mix the stain. While you can buy prepared color stains, it might be better to mix it yourself. For a primer stain mix an equal amount of linseed oil and turpentine in a can (one pint will be enough for a piece of furniture) and add oil color pigments from small tubes. For a birch finish use small amounts of white, yellow and brown, mixed thoroughly.

Prepare the furniture. Take out the drawers, remove all hardware and drawer knobs. Sand lightly with 3/0 sandpaper held around a sanding block. Clean off the dust inside and out with a dry brush and a slightly dampened cloth.

Now apply the stain. Use only a good quality bristle brush, 3 or 4 inches wide. First coat the sides of the cabinet, then the top, and finally the narrow drawer edges.

Don't pile up blobs of stain here and there—dip the brush frequently, but lightly into the can. Work in the stain so the brush becomes almost dry, and run the brush only *with* the wood grain. Stain one section at a time, ending each part by running the brush clear across the surface out beyond the end, all in a single stroke without stopping. This will prevent smearing any one spot. Make sure the entire surface is smoothly and uniformly coated.

When the cabinet is done, do the drawer fronts, then the knobs. Let the furniture dry at least a full day in a dust-free room.

Unfinished pine cabinets should be stained before finishing. Start by sanding all surfaces.

See chart (page 290) for some popular finishing colors. Stains are mixed with oil and turpentine.

289

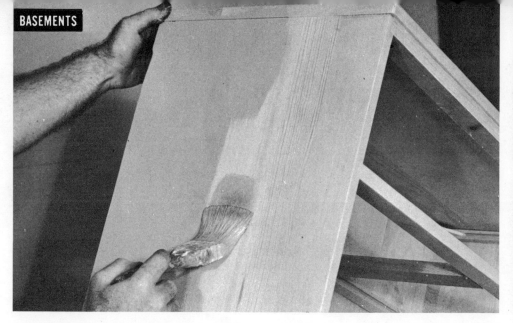

Apply stain with thickly bristled brush, working it out smoothly in the direction of wood grain.

When dry give all parts a vigorous sanding with 3/0 garnet paper to remove brush marks and air blisters. Wipe clean and coat with shellac.

After the final coat of shellac, sand again in preparation for the final rubbing. Mix pumice powder in rubbing oil to a stiff consistency and apply with 00 steel wool. Rub *with* the grain, applying sufficient pressure to bring out a high gloss and to remove any possible surface blemishes.

Wipe the surface carefully with a cloth to remove all traces of the pumice and oil, and finish with a rubbed coat of paste wax. If done correctly the furniture will have a smooth, hard surface, and the pine grain will be subdued so that the appearance will be that of birch or maple, adding to the decorative values of what started out as a low-cost pine cabinet.

PINE FINISHES

Silver Sierra: Brush on flat white undercoat paint with a touch of lead blue added. Wipe off and let dry. Apply clear finish (lacquer, varnish or shellac) to surface or wax.

Feather River Fawn: Brush on equal parts lead blue, burnt umber thinned with mineral thinner. Wipe off and let dry. Apply clear finish to surface or wax.

Clearwater Natural: One coat lacquer sealer; sand with 6/0 paper then apply a minimum of two coats of selected clear varnish, shellac or lacquer, rubbing with 3/0 steel wool after each coat.

Colorado Coffee: Brush on equal parts burnt umber and chrome yellow. Thin lightly with mineral thinner to leave darker stain. Wipe off and let dry. Apply clear finish to surface or wax.

Kaibab Sage: Brush on equal parts lead blue paint, burnt umber and yellow chrome with a mineral thinner. Wipe off and let dry. Apply clear finish to surface or wax.

Bitterroot Buff: Brush on mixture of flat white undercoat paint tinted with lead blue and burnt umber color in oil. Wipe off and let dry. Apply clear finish to surface or wax.

Sundance Yellow: Mix chrome yellow in mineral thinner to stainlike consistency. Apply liberally with brush, getting full coverage, then immediately wipe dry with soft cloth. Apply clear finish or wax.

Blue Mountain: Mix Prussian blue with paint thinner until it is of stainlike consistency. Brush on liberally, then wipe off. Let dry a few minutes, then rub lightly with 4/0 steel wool to bring out grain. Apply clear finish or wax.

Butte Valley Brown: Mix one part black oil paint with two parts gold paint. Brush on paneling liberally, then immediately wipe off. Let dry, then apply clear finish or wax.

Deschutes Dawn: Mix four parts aluminum (silver) paint with one part red color in oil. Brush onto wood, immediately wipe off with soft cloth. Let dry. Apply clear finish or wax.

Tuolumne Tawn: Brush on liberal amounts of aluminum (silver) paint, then wipe off immediately with soft cloth. Allow to dry, then apply clear finish or wax.

Note: Above are just some of the possible finishes that can be obtained on knotty pine.

Sand unit after stain is dry. Apply three coats of shellac, sanding lightly between each coat.

For final rubbing mix pumice powder in acid-free oil, using fine steel wool for satin sheen.

Last step consists of polishing with paste wax. Pine now has smooth, hard surface.

Floors and Ceilings

For most ceiling installations, 1x3 furring strips are first attached to basement joists.

BASEMENT and attic ceiling tiles are put up after the walls are finished but before floor tiles are laid. One reason for this schedule is that the fiber tiles with which most ceilings are finished are quite soft and might be soiled or damaged during wall or floor construction.

For all materials, except knotty pine, the ceiling is furred out with 1x2-inch strips nailed across the joists and around all wall projections. Then the tongue-and-groove insulating tiles are put up, either with nails or a stapling gun.

The only difficulty that might be encountered is the rare condition where joists are not level, and require shimming of the wood strips. Also, where plumbing pipes run across the joists it will be necessary to build out the furring for clearance.

If the joists are particularly high, or ceiling height varies in different parts of the room, it is possible to drop and "suspend" the ceiling by nailing 4- or 6-inch lengths of 1x2s, at right angles (vertical) to the joists. Horizontal furring strips are then nailed or screwed to these

Installation of acoustical ceiling tiles and decorative plastic flooring will give your downstairs room that final luxurious touch.

Some tiles are installed with blobs of adhesive and nailed against furring or hardboard panels.

Surface must be level. Press tile against the ceiling panel and butt against adjoining tile.

Other types of tiles have tongue-and-groove edges which interlock. Here, nail through the tongue.

Staples may also be used for quicker installation; glue is not necessary with these ceiling tiles.

uprights. Ceiling tiles are quite light in weight, and they will be "tied" together by their tongue-and-groove joints in the process of installation.

Whatever material you use for the ceiling, there is one rule that applies to all: arrange the furring so the space at the end walls is equalized, i.e., of sufficient distance from both side walls. This precaution will help prevent a situation where the ceiling tiles at one side must be cut to only an inch or two in width while the opposite side is a full 12 or 16 inches.

Measuring beforehand will let you know how it will work out; if necessary, start one side closer to the wall than the normal 12 inches, so the tiles on the opposite side will be about equal width.

Materials generally used for ceiling finishes are:

Gypsum board, in large-size panels, nailed to the furring or sometimes directly over the joists. The panels are quite heavy so you'll need help to hold up one end while you tack the other. For one-man installation, use a ceiling-height brace to

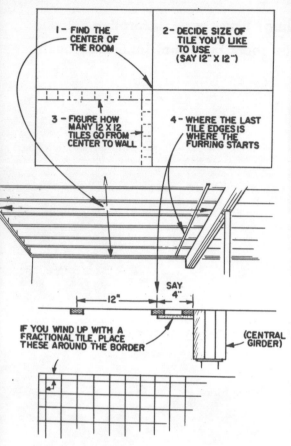

1 - FIND THE CENTER OF THE ROOM

2 - DECIDE SIZE OF TILE YOU'D LIKE TO USE (SAY 12" X 12")

3 - FIGURE HOW MANY 12 X 12 TILES GO FROM CENTER TO WALL

4 - WHERE THE LAST TILE EDGE IS WHERE THE FURRING STARTS

SAY 4"

12"

IF YOU WIND UP WITH A FRACTIONAL TILE, PLACE THESE AROUND THE BORDER

(CENTRAL GIRDER)

Tongue-and-groove Celotex tiles are easy to install, and may be cut to fit around obstructions.

support the panel. Smaller panels such as 4x4 feet, will be easier to handle. Nailing is similar to that for wall panels, closely spaced so the heavy panels won't sag. Gypsum board may be covered with wallpaper when taped and shackled, or used as a backing for application of plastic tiles.

Laminated building board. These are lighter in weight and much easier to handle than gypsum board, but must go up absolutely level and well-nailed.

Ceiling tile—insulating tongue-and-groove fiberboard in plain acoustical types, ½ inch thick. Pre-finished in white or

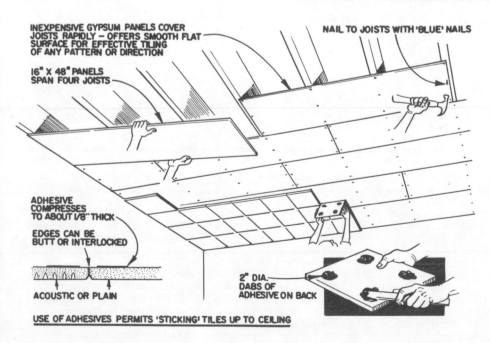

INEXPENSIVE GYPSUM PANELS COVER JOISTS RAPIDLY - OFFERS SMOOTH FLAT SURFACE FOR EFFECTIVE TILING OF ANY PATTERN OR DIRECTION

16" X 48" PANELS SPAN FOUR JOISTS

NAIL TO JOISTS WITH 'BLUE' NAILS

ADHESIVE COMPRESSES TO ABOUT 1/8 THICK

EDGES CAN BE BUTT OR INTERLOCKED

ACOUSTIC OR PLAIN

2" DIA. DABS OF ADHESIVE ON BACK

USE OF ADHESIVES PERMITS 'STICKING' TILES UP TO CEILING

Photo shows the staggered method used to obtain decorative effect. Note furring strip location.

Above, complete section of ceiling covered with
acoustical squares. Tiles at the edge are shorter.

pastel shades, some with interesting designs. May be re-painted. Acoustical
type has closely spaced holes partway
through material. Use with 3-penny
blued nails or staples. Sizes: 12x12 inches,
12x24 inches, 16x16 inches and 16x32
inches.

Knotty Pine. Widely favored for ceilings. Easy to install, the tongue-and-
groove pine boards have good insulating
value, can be conveniently pre-finished
before installation to match the walls, or
in contrasting shades. No furring is necessary if the joists are reasonably level.
Boards in uniform or random widths up to

1x12 inches are blind nailed through the
tongues into the joists. Board ends are
butted together, but try to alternate the
positions of these joints by starting with
different lengths at one end of the room so
that joints will not be too prominent.

Plastic tiles, squares, etc. Rigid plastic
tiles are installed with mastic adhesive
against a smooth gypsum or hardboard
backing. These tiles, in a great range of
colors, are particularly effective in areas
where there is excessive moisture such as
a laundry or bathroom. They are popular
also for playrooms and attic bedrooms because of cleanliness and decorative value.

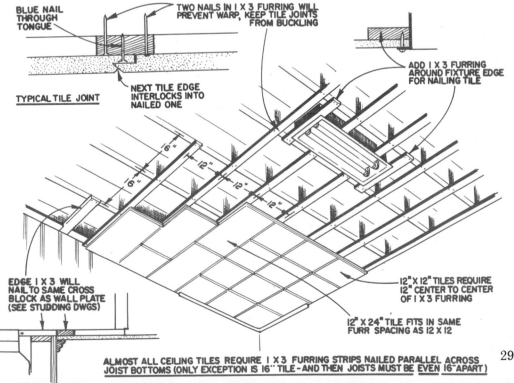

BLUE NAIL
THROUGH
TONGUE

TWO NAILS IN 1 X 3 FURRING WILL
PREVENT WARP, KEEP TILE JOINTS
FROM BUCKLING

ADD 1 X 3 FURRING
AROUND FIXTURE EDGE
FOR NAILING TILE

TYPICAL TILE JOINT

NEXT TILE EDGE
INTERLOCKS INTO
NAILED ONE

EDGE 1 X 3 WILL
NAIL TO SAME CROSS
BLOCK AS WALL PLATE
(SEE STUDDING DWGS)

12" X 12" TILES REQUIRE
12" CENTER TO CENTER
OF 1 X 3 FURRING

12" X 24" TILE FITS IN SAME
FURR SPACING AS 12 X 12

ALMOST ALL CEILING TILES REQUIRE 1 X 3 FURRING STRIPS NAILED PARALLEL ACROSS
JOIST BOTTOMS (ONLY EXCEPTION IS 16" TILE - AND THEN JOISTS MUST BE EVEN 16" APART)

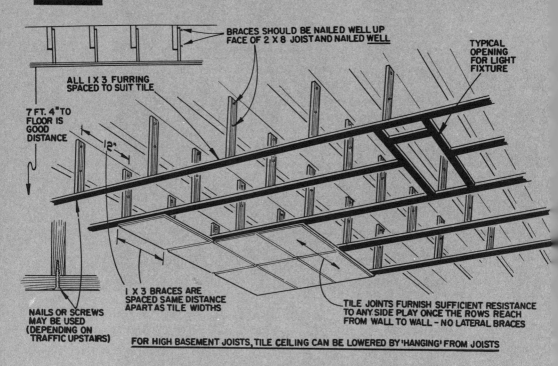

BRACES SHOULD BE NAILED WELL UP FACE OF 2 X 8 JOIST AND NAILED <u>WELL</u>

TYPICAL OPENING FOR LIGHT FIXTURE

ALL I X 3 FURRING SPACED TO SUIT TILE

7 FT. 4" TO FLOOR IS GOOD DISTANCE

12"

NAILS OR SCREWS MAY BE USED (DEPENDING ON TRAFFIC UPSTAIRS)

I X 3 BRACES ARE SPACED SAME DISTANCE APART AS TILE WIDTHS

TILE JOINTS FURNISH SUFFICIENT RESISTANCE TO ANY SIDE PLAY ONCE THE ROWS REACH FROM WALL TO WALL – NO LATERAL BRACES

<u>FOR HIGH BASEMENT JOISTS, TILE CEILING CAN BE LOWERED BY 'HANGING' FROM JOISTS</u>

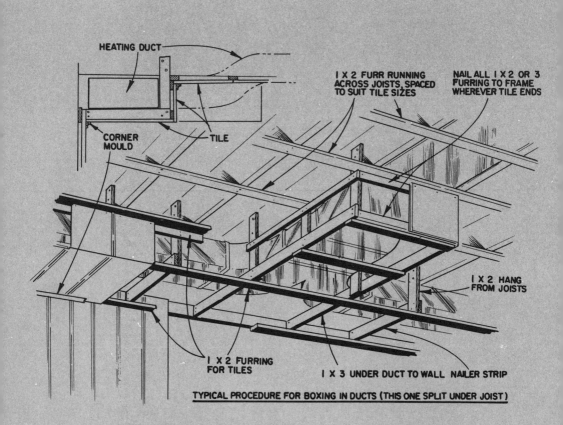

HEATING DUCT

I X 2 FURR RUNNING ACROSS JOISTS, SPACED TO SUIT TILE SIZES

NAIL ALL I X 2 OR 3 FURRING TO FRAME WHEREVER TILE ENDS

CORNER MOULD

TILE

I X 2 HANG FROM JOISTS

I X 2 FURRING FOR TILES

I X 3 UNDER DUCT TO WALL   NAILER STRIP

<u>TYPICAL PROCEDURE FOR BOXING IN DUCTS (THIS ONE SPLIT UNDER JOIST)</u>

Floor Installation

Wood floors formerly were installed over scrads or "sleepers" and had the disadvantage that any water or moisture that ran on the floor was trapped and soaked into the 2x4 sleepers. The result was wood rot, dampness and unpleasant odors.

A better method where wood floors are desired, as in a basement guest bedroom, is the use of laminated oak blocks, ½ inch thick, over a layer of special mastic. The wood floor, however, may be installed only where there is no moisture problem, either through condensation or seepage. Correct waterproofing of the concrete slab with polyethylene film and use of the proper mastic will then assure an effective installation.

Newest item for basement floors is vinyl-asbestos tile which is better looking, more durable. The vinyl tiles are not affected by paint solvents, are easier to clean and can be installed directly over concrete below grade or in any room of the house.

Most floor tiles come in 9x9-inch size. When figuring the quantity required for your room allow about 10% extra for waste and to fit around the wall borders.

Remember to spread the adhesive with a notched trowel as specified by the manufacturer. Too much adhesive will cause seepage or "bleeding" between the joints and also may cause cracking of the tiles.

First step is to inspect the concrete floor and correct conditions that will affect the final tile surface. Each indentation or projection on the concrete will show up later

Cracks in basement floor should be widened, repaired with filler compound and sanded smooth.

Where part of floor dips in a corner, you can raise its pitch with application of floor cement.

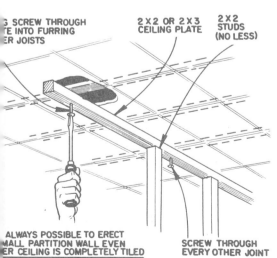

SCREW THROUGH E INTO FURRING ER JOISTS

2 X 2 OR 2 X 3 CEILING PLATE

2 X 2 STUDS (NO LESS)

ALWAYS POSSIBLE TO ERECT MALL PARTITION WALL EVEN ER CEILING IS COMPLETELY TILED

SCREW THROUGH EVERY OTHER JOINT

If entire floor is uneven, best cure is resurfacing with Flormastic compound. Mix in crude box.

in the tiles. Use a chisel to chop off any pebbles or lumps of concrete, then mix up some cement and fill every small hole.

If the floor is uneven, it should be straightened out with underlayment compound which consists of 1½ parts Armstrong's Flormastic, 1 part lumnite cement and 3 parts clean fine sand. All floor cracks, expansion joints and holes should be filled and troweled smooth.

Where the floor is wavy or very rough, a complete application of underlayment

Apply Flormastic compound as you would portland cement. Use guides, level off surface with striking board.

For heavy duty floors, workshops, etc., additional strength may be gained by reinforcing the compound with a single layer of chicken wire.

Use steel trowel to obtain as smooth a surface as possible for perfect tile installation. Most tile or linoleum damage results from uneven base.

fill is required. To do this, start with a priming coat of Flormastic thinned with water to brushing consistency. Spread with a paint or scrubbing brush. Then apply the floor fill with a float and trowel, using a straightedge to assure level surface. If there is a floor drain, use a spirit level to determine the direction of pitch down to the drain. Follow with a coat of Armstrong's No. S-80 floor primer.

Paint and varnish must be entirely removed from the floor; otherwise the tile adhesive won't "take." Methods for removal vary according to the type of paint. Sanding machines, blow torch or paint remover chemicals are effective, but most paint removers are toxic and highly inflammable and extreme caution is suggested when used in a closed room. A better method of removing floor paint is a strong solution of tri-sodium phosphate in water, spread over the floor.

The solution is allowed to remain on the floor for an hour or so, then rinsed with clear water. You'll be able to do this effectively only if the cellar has a floor drain.

Your floor must be completely dry before you proceed with applying the adhesive. Do about half the floor at a time, allowing to dry sufficiently so there is no tackiness—this takes at least half an hour in heated rooms. Start at the center of the room, working toward the walls. The border tiles are installed last.

For comprehensive data on installing your floor tiles, write to Armstrong Cork Co., Lancaster, Pa., for a copy of the booklet *How to Install Excelong Tile*. Before installing any wood floor, obtain a copy of the booklet *How to Install Bruce Block Floors* by writing to E. L. Bruce Co., Memphis 1, Tennessee.

For tile installation, measure room, find the center and mark as shown. Apply recommended paste.

Spread paste with special applicator, a small area at a time, and press tiles into position.

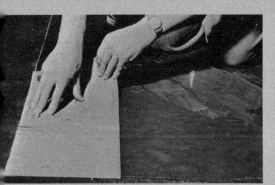

Tiles are started at middle of floor and worked out toward wall. Finish one quarter of room first.

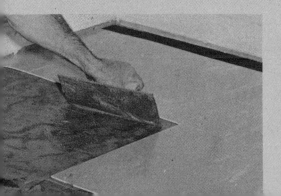

Many types of plastic flooring materials are available, and all are durable and easy to maintain.

Stairs and Entrances

Follow some of the suggestions given here on building, repairing and decorating of stairs—an important part of your basement project.

WHEN your basement is finished it becomes part of the living space of your home—in fact, you may well find that it becomes the most popular part of the house, particularly if it has a TV or audio system.

The staircase, then, must be safe and sound. Formerly it may not have mattered if steps were somewhat rickety and the railing nonexistent. But now, these neglected items must be taken care of to avoid serious accidents.

Go over the staircase carefully; check all the treads to see that they are solid. Wedge them in tightly; reinforce the handrail, or replace it with a new one of more sturdy and attractive design. Enclosing the bottom of the staircase with a solid framework of 2x3s will help shore up the stairs and give a more secure footing.

Other improvements will be to cover the treads with linoleum or tiles to create a pleasant design for the staircase itself, making it part of the new surroundings.

Open-view dowel stairs are a welcome change from conventional handrails and spindles. An added feature is that the clothes-pole dowels are readily removable to give more clearance when bulky furniture must be carried up or down.

Only two 1x6-inch boards are needed for the project: one for the top plate that is nailed to the ceiling; the other is fitted to the stair stringer. The two-inch dowels, spaced about ten inches apart, are drilled at the bottom to fit into the smaller pin

dowels that lock them securely in place.

The ceiling plate is drilled for two-inch holes at positions equal to the front edge of the stair treads. The same expansive bit is used to extend the holes into ceiling tiles for a depth of one inch. If the ceiling is of plaster, the hole is deepened with a cold chisel instead of the bit.

The bottom plate is nailed directly to the stair stringer and a plumb line is dropped from each top hole to show positions for drilling this plate.

Holes, here, must be drilled at an angle that will be in vertical alignment with the poles. Short pegs of ¾-inch dowel are glued into the holes, and the pole dowels drilled at the bottom to fit over these locking pegs. The poles also must be angle-sawed at the ends to match the incline of the stringer board.

The only tricky part is boring holes in the pole ends for the locking pins. A jig devised for this purpose will take you just minutes to make. Use a board about 4 inches wide, 4 inches long. Nail a 1x1-inch strip along one side, place a length of the pole dowel against the first side, and nail another strip snug against the other side of the pole.

At one end of the jig build up a platform using a piece of 1-inch stock to guide the bit (preferably a power auger) at a level that will find the center of the dowel. You may have to groove this resting block to obtain correct level. Two wood strips at the sides of this platform will keep the

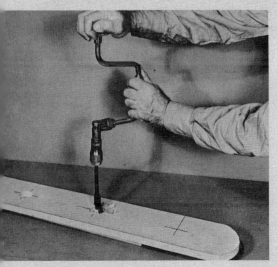

Ceiling plate above stairway is drilled with holes spaced about 10" apart to receive dowels.

Nail top plate to ceiling and drop plumb line from each hole. Mark location and drill stringer.

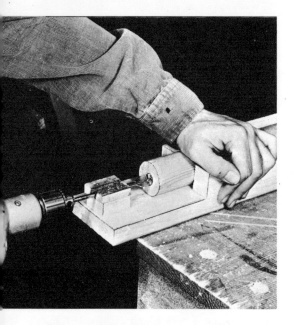

Holes are drilled into the dowel to receive the smaller locking dowels which are set in stairs.

Small, ¾" locking dowel is glued into stringer plate. See drawing, right, for mounting details.

To cover stairs with linoleum or tile treads, start by cutting the metal nose molding to length.

Attach nose molding with nails or screws. Nail-heads will be later covered by linoleum or tiles.

drill from wobbling once it starts into the hole.

The pole dowels are drilled first at one end with the jig, then angle-cut to fit. Best way is to hold your saw miter gauge against the stair stringer, adjust the runner plumb by means of a spirit level, and lock the gauge. This gives a setting equal to the incline of the stair stringer. When you run the dowel (the end that has been drilled) through the saw, the angle will be correct to fit the stairs. Drill the dowels before sawing the ends.

The short poles at the top of the stairs need not be removable, and thus may be installed by merely sawing the ends to correct angle and fastening them with screws through the stringer underneath.

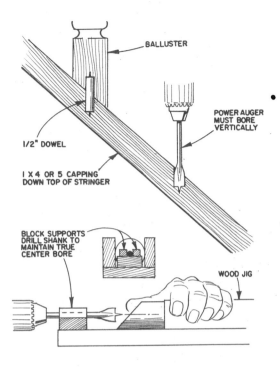

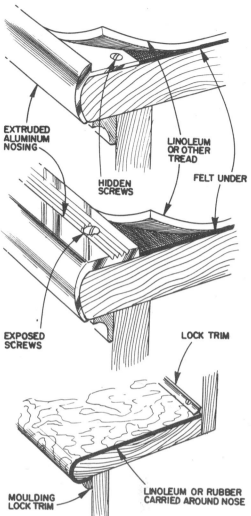

Cut felt paper to size to fit on both tread and riser; the felt permits easy removal of covering.

The poles are removed by lifting them into the recess space at the ceiling so the bottom clears the pins; they are replaced quickly in the same manner. You will find that the poles, when in place, are securely held at top and bottom and won't wobble. A hand railing, however, should be placed on the opposite wall.

An interesting decorative note is ob-

Special linoleum adhesive is spread on the wood steps and back of felt. Remove all excess paste.

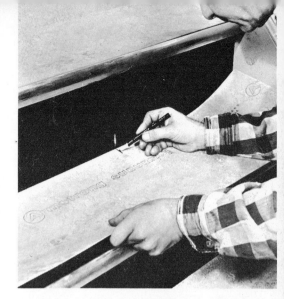

Use a roller or tap down with wood block to assure good, even adhesion of felt strip. Allow to dry.

Cut the linoleum slightly oversize for a tight fit. Mark center line on both riser and linoleum.

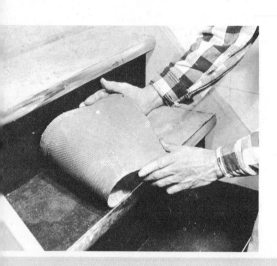

Again, use special adhesive spreader for proper distribution of paste on linoleum or tile back.

Fit front edge tightly against molding and roll linoleum to eliminate all air bubbles underneath.

Chrome cove molding hides space between stair and riser covering, adds to general appearance.

tained by painting the stair poles in contrasting colors, with a loop of heavy rope at the bottom of each pole.

Uncovered wood stairs tend to wear quickly and unevenly. Homeowners should cover the stairs with practical flooring material such as linoleum or tiles, properly cemented down. Small rubber stair treads often tear free of their tacks and create a hazard.

Linoleum is favored because it is quite resilient, has good traction and can be put down in one piece. With linoleum, a flange-type metal nosing is used on the

New basement stairs can easily be built with stringers supported by 2x4 framing along the sides. Handrail is also made of 2x4 lumber. Gypsum board is used to cover and close in both sides of the staircase.

Photo right shows interesting treatment of basement end of stairs, permitting two-way approach.

tread, leaving only a thin edge bead of metal exposed. Asphalt or vinyl-asbestos tiles require a butt-type molding which has a wider metal surface at the top; this edge is deeply ridged, however, for secure traction. Tile is used generally when you desire to match the floor design.

The stair treads and risers should both be covered with the same material for good appearance and easy cleaning, but the risers may be of contrasting color.

If stair treads are in good condition, go right ahead with the installation. First cut the nosings to length with a hacksaw

Outside steel hatch entrance is valuable asset to any basement, allows entrance of bulky supplies.

Areaway (see drawing) is dug first, then a wall opening is cut into the basement foundation blocks.

Cinder or cement blocks are used to erect the three-sided areaway. Footing is poured concrete.

and attach them to the step treads with screws. Measure carefully to get a good fit; use an extension-type folding rule if you have one.

Next apply the felt lining. Cut the felt to approximate size, place one straight factory-cut edge against the riser, cut to fit at the sides of the step and in back of the metal nosing. At this point, stop and check the gauge of your material against the molding; it should slip against the curved bead and be flush with the molding surface. If too high, put down felt only to the edge

of the molding; if too low, put lining felt all the way to the front edge of the molding to equalize thickness.

Continue to cut pieces of felt for all the risers and treads; and paste down with your adhesive.

Linoleum now is cut for the steps. You could measure the size of each tread, and cut the linoleum with a knife against a straightedge. But the linoleum must fit perfectly on all sides; otherwise dirt and water will collect in any openings. As each step likely has some variation in size, and

Blocks rise just above grade level. Steel stair stringers attach to blocks with masonry anchors.

Waterproof the walls with asphalt compound. Hatchway frame is supported temporarily on rocks.

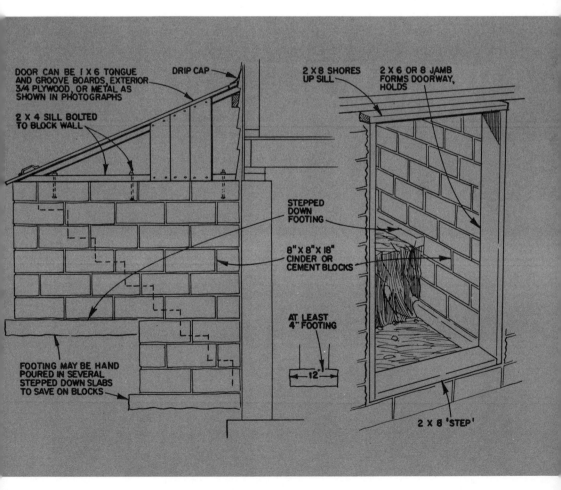

DOOR CAN BE 1 X 6 TONGUE AND GROOVE BOARDS, EXTERIOR 3/4 PLYWOOD, OR METAL AS SHOWN IN PHOTOGRAPHS

DRIP CAP

2 X 4 SILL BOLTED TO BLOCK WALL

FOOTING MAY BE HAND POURED IN SEVERAL STEPPED DOWN SLABS TO SAVE ON BLOCKS

2 X 8 SHORES UP SILL

2 X 6 OR 8 JAMB FORMS DOORWAY, HOLDS

STEPPED DOWN FOOTING

8" X 8" X 18" CINDER OR CEMENT BLOCKS

AT LEAST 4" FOOTING

12"

2 X 8 'STEP'

Attach rear of hatchway frame to house wall and fill in area all around cinder blocks.

Hatchway cover in place supported by rocks at front. Note space between metal frame and blocks.

Space between frame and blocks is now filled in with concrete. Construct wooden frame for pouring.

may even be warped or curved, it is best to fit each strip right on the step.

Cut oversize strips of linoleum, place the factory-cut edge against the rise with ends folded over for clearance. Mark a line near the center from linoleum to riser. Lay one end flat against a side, use a scriber or compass opened to width equal to the space between the marked lines. Cut along the scribed line and that end should fit perfectly against the side. Do the other side the same way.

Spread adhesive with the trowel, either on the steps or directly on the linoleum strips, and lay in the linoleum. Roll it out for good adhesion with a rolling pin.

The risers are fitted in similar manner. The joint where riser and tread meet should be covered with strips of chromium or plastic cove molding, fastened with oval-head screws.

Now, what if the wood steps had been badly worn or corrugated? Application of floor fill will level them off. The floor fill consists of Armstrong's Flormastic mixed with Lumnite cement and clean sand. The mixture is 1½ parts Flormastic, 1 part cement and 3 parts sand. Clean steps thoroughly, apply fill with trowel and allow to dry completely before proceeding with the linoleum installation.

One of the biggest obstacles to making full use of basement space is lack of a convenient entrance. In many homes, the cellar stairs are so placed that the upstairs entrance has very little clearance—perhaps a near-by wall is in the way to prevent carrying down any lumber or furniture

of any size. Some stairways have little headroom so you have to duck a beam every time you go up or down.

Best solution is to install an outside staircase that offers easy entrance, is large enough so you can carry in panels and chairs and tools, even a piano. This seems like a big job, but that's not necessarily so. The reason is that a prefabricated steel hatchway minimizes the work and cost, and speeds the installation. A contractor will do this job for you for approximately $300. This figure can be chopped down considerably if you are willing to do the work yourself.

The process starts with excavating the area to be occupied by the cellar entrance and breaking an opening in the wall. Professional contractors equipped with special pneumatic hammers will go through any wall and the job will take barely an hour. The excavated well is built up with concrete blocks above grade level; the metal stringers are anchored to the inside walls and 2x10-inch wood steps attached.

Metal doors are then fitted above the opening to seal out the weather, with poured concrete between the block wall and the doors. No floor drain is needed at the bottom, if you are careful to keep the doors closed.

At the cellar wall opening, steel door buck is set in, the sides patched and calked with cement mortar, and a door fitted into the buck. Detailed specifications and complete installation sketches may be obtained by writing to The Bilco Company, New Haven, Conn. •

Steps under hatch may be concrete, wood or metal. See drawing, right, for concrete construction.

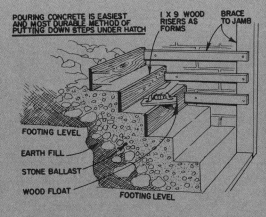

POURING CONCRETE IS EASIEST AND MOST DURABLE METHOD OF PUTTING DOWN STEPS UNDER HATCH

1 X 9 WOOD RISERS AS FORMS

BRACE TO JAMB

FOOTING LEVEL

EARTH FILL

STONE BALLAST

WOOD FLOAT

FOOTING LEVEL

PRIMPING is real fun for a teenager in this decorative "powder room," revamped by Daddy.

Your Bathroom
Can Be Beautiful!

The most used part of the house is worth dolling up.

THE splash and spatter of children getting ready to make the school bus, of Daddy getting ready for work, the rush to get cleaned up and off to fun or entertainment, the smears and bumps of toddlers . . . all are enough to reduce the ordinary bathroom to a shambles within a very short span of time.

We have four children, so our bathroom became "old" in just about one year of occupancy of a new house. Since

we like our home to look presentable, we decided that ordinary wall paper, shower curtains, etc., were just not the answer. We determined to find out what was.

One of the first things we decided to replace was the wallpaper. We used Cortina "Marble" Lamidall, which is a material ⅛ in. thick and which comes in panels. The tough plastic decorative surface is available in patterns as well

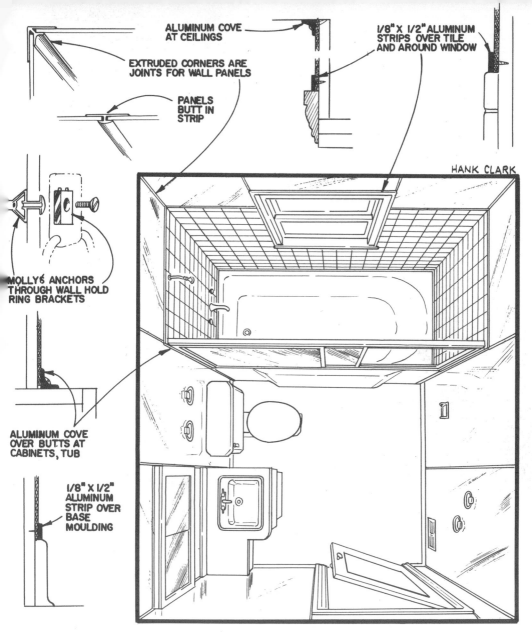

ALUMINUM COVE AT CEILINGS

EXTRUDED CORNERS ARE JOINTS FOR WALL PANELS

PANELS BUTT IN STRIP

1/8" X 1/2" ALUMINUM STRIPS OVER TILE AND AROUND WINDOW

HANK CLARK

MOLLY6 ANCHORS THROUGH WALL HOLD RING BRACKETS

ALUMINUM COVE OVER BUTTS AT CABINETS, TUB

1/8" X 1/2" ALUMINUM STRIP OVER BASE MOULDING

TYPICAL bathroom, as viewed from above. Tub is in corner, and lends itself readily to addition of sliding-door enclosure. Aluminum molding permits neat installation of new wall panels.

as in marble designs, and is bonded to a Masonite Tempered Duolux base. Formica and similar materials are also suitable. It is wise to check the properties, availability and cost of the various types of paneling in your shopping area.

One of the best ways to remove old wallpaper is with warm water and a wide putty knife. Begin at one end of a wall. Sponge on the water from top to bottom, working in vertical strips about two feet wide. Keep rags or old towels along the floor to prevent seepage to rooms below. It may require several applications to soften the old paste sufficiently. Where there are several layers of paper (a possibility in a house that has been decorated more than once), remove them one at a time.

Some wallpaper is coated in manufacture with a varnish or plastic to make it waterproof or at least water resist-

OLD WALLPAPER is softened with water and removed with putty knife or other scraper.

CUTOUTS in new wall paneling are best made with a saber saw, with sharp blade.

MOLDING strips, for new wall panels, are fastened securely by screws and anchors.

A SHORT MOLDING strip is being positioned here against a panel, to assure fit.

ant. The coating must be removed or loosened by sanding, to allow the water to penetrate and to loosen the paste underneath. After all the paper is off, sponge the wall down with clean water to remove any residue.

If you are putting up the permanent type of finish shown in the accompanying illustrations and are concerned simply with providing a good "sticking" surface for the panel adhesive, the old wallpaper may be scraped or sanded off dry. The ideal tool for this job is a portable power sander. It kicks up a lot of dust, so keep a vacuum cleaner handy. Finish off with 3/0 sandpaper.

If the walls are only painted, they may be sanded and then wiped clean with benzine or turpentine. Don't smoke when working with benzine, and keep the window open for ventilation. High and low spots on the wall should be sanded smooth, and hollows filled in with some form of patching plaster.

When Lamidall panels are to be used as wall covering they should be pre-expanded. Pick an open floor area in the basement and cover it with newspapers, rags, or an old blanket. Place one sheet finish face down on the covering. Wet the back well with a broom, mop or brush. Wet the back of another panel and place it down on the first one. Continue wetting and stacking the panels back to back. Cover them with more paper, a tarpaulin, an old poncho or shelter half, etc., and keep them that way for 24 hours prior to installation.

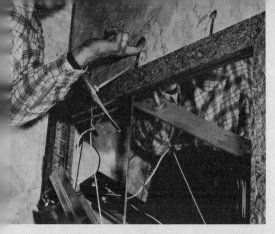

HOLES in panel above medicine cabinet are for wires and studs of lighting fixture.

BLACK PLASTIC towel rings swivel freely on metal mounts; they assemble readily.

MOUNTING BASES of towel rings are anchored securely by mollys and screws.

HIGH ring is for large bath towels, lower one for smaller hand and face towels.

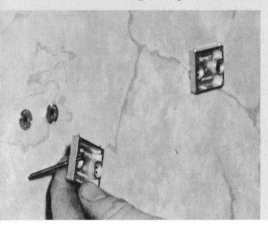

Always saw, drill or otherwise cut the panels with the face side up. An ordinary pencil hardly makes an impression on the surface; instead, use a "China marking" or "negative" grease pencil. The lines made by these pencils can be rubbed off with the fingertips.

The panels as we received them were covered with cellophane or some similar plastic, evidently for protection of the face surface. It was possible to do most of the marking and cutting with the cellophane in place; in fact, it wasn't peeled off until the panels were almost completely installed.

All moldings must be cut to proper size before the panels are mounted. Be careful not to jam the panels tightly against each other or against the ceiling or bottom base at the floor line.

Leave approximately 1/32-in. border all around for expansion. Aluminum or stainless steel moldings with recessed lips make clean and neat joints possible along walls and in corners. After applying adhesive and putting corner molding in place, put one edge of a panel into the recessed lip of the molding but do not force it too far. By hand, press the panel firmly against the wall, working over the whole area several times to make sure that you don't miss any spots.

Countersunk holes must be made in molding flanges for flathead wood screws in cases where a strip falls over a stud. If a position is not over a stud and you feel it desirable to screw the molding to the wall, in addition to ce-

"GRAB" TYPE catch keeps bathroom door open when ventilation and light are wanted.

FRAME of tub enclosure is marked out very accurately in advance of drilling of holes.

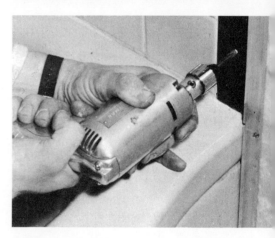

WITH TUB frame lined up, hole locations for screws are marked with grease crayon.

GLAZIER'S drill in hand power tool makes short work of holes in hard tile surface.

ILLUSTRATING two types of molding fasteners. Lead core anchors take common wood screws; mollys, bolts.

THOROUGH sealing of mounting rails prevents shower water from leaking over top of tub to the floor.

SECTIONS OF tub enclosure frame are reinforced by end tabs. These are bent with screwdriver.

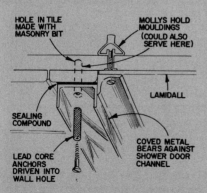

HOLE IN TILE MADE WITH MASONRY BIT

MOLLYS HOLD MOULDINGS (COULD ALSO SERVE HERE)

LAMIDALL

SEALING COMPOUND

LEAD CORE ANCHORS DRIVEN INTO WALL HOLE

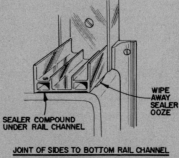

WIPE AWAY SEALER OOZE

SEALER COMPOUND UNDER RAIL CHANNEL

COVED METAL BEARS AGAINST SHOWER DOOR CHANNEL

JOINT OF SIDES TO BOTTOM RAIL CHANNEL

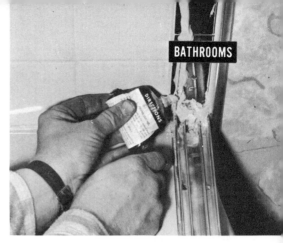

FIBER-COVERED lead plugs are tapped gently into holes. They take ordinary screws.

SEALING COMPOUND is run along area to be covered by enclosure mounting frame.

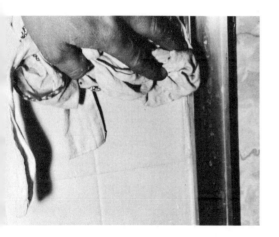

EXCESS SEALER is wiped off with rag after all strips have been screwed in place.

SETTLEMENT cracks along bottom of bathtub are filled with sealer to improve looks.

menting it, use molly anchors with machine screws to fit.

To allow installation of paneling over the medicine cabinet, the light fixture was removed but the electrical connections were left intact. For safety's sake, remove the fuse for this circuit. Don't take any chances with live wires in a bathroom. Every piece of plumbing is part of the "ground" circuit and is potentially dangerous in relation to exposed wires.

Semicircular, solid black plastic towel rings were mounted on the wall near the tub by means of molly anchors. These fixtures replaced conventional towel bars on the back of the door which were continually falling off because the mounting screws did not hold in the thin veneer facing of the door.

The latter was taken off its hinges,

EXTRA towel bar on sliding door of tub enclosure is handy for family and guests.

MITERED corners of molding around paper holder are filled with aluminum paste.

AFTER DRYING, excess filler is cleaned off and polished well with fine steel wool.

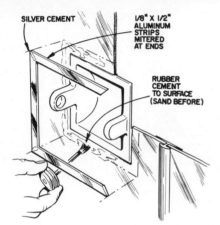

SILVER CEMENT

1/8" X 1/2" ALUMINUM STRIPS MITERED AT ENDS

RUBBER CEMENT TO SURFACE (SAND BEFORE)

LEFT: Since there is no actual strain on it, molding for paper holder, soap dish, etc., can be attached with cement. Facing surfaces must be roughened slightly with sandpaper to offer "tooth" for adhesive.

BELOW: Basin build-up provides drawer, at left, and large storage space, bottom. Latter is particularly useful for bulky items such as toilet rolls and facial tissues and economy size bottles of shampoos, etc.

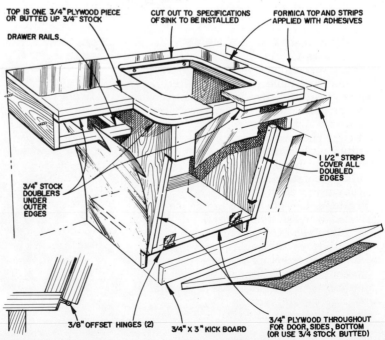

TOP IS ONE 3/4" PLYWOOD PIECE OR BUTTED UP 3/4" STOCK

CUT OUT TO SPECIFICATIONS OF SINK TO BE INSTALLED

FORMICA TOP AND STRIPS APPLIED WITH ADHESIVES

DRAWER RAILS

1 1/2" STRIPS COVER ALL DOUBLED EDGES

3/4" STOCK DOUBLERS UNDER OUTER EDGES

3/8" OFFSET HINGES (2)

3/4" X 3" KICK BOARD

3/4" PLYWOOD THROUGHOUT FOR DOOR, SIDES, BOTTOM (OR USE 3/4 STOCK BUTTED)

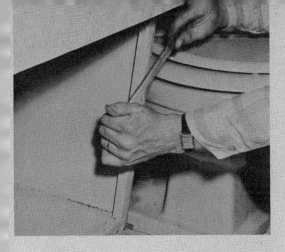

EXPOSED edges of paneling are smoothed with light file strokes in one direction only.

COMPLETELY revamped basin section looks attractive, is waterproof, and easy to clean.

sanded to remove the cheap shellac applied by the builder, and re-covered with Fabulon. It also could have been finished with Min-Wax, varnish or lacquer.

The hinges were oiled and the door replaced. We then found that it would not stay open. During the winter months, this door is often kept closed to confine heat in the bathroom, but during the summer it is left open for additional ventilation and light from an adjacent hallway. You may like the same arrangement. If so, it is wise to install a "grab" type door stop. In our house, the larger member was put on the inside of the door (in an area where there is solid core), while the smaller member was mounted on the bathroom wall by means of a molly.

Unless a stud was there to receive wood screws, mollys were used again to fasten cove molding which was run from the tile baseboard, up along the tub, along the outside face of the tower enclosure and up to the top border of the tile. The mounting instructions supplied with the tub enclosure were followed faithfully.

Ordinary drills are ruined quickly if they are used on tile. However, a glass cutter's drill goes through as if the material were so much cheese.

Since most tile by nature is somewhat fragile, it is advisable to experiment on scrap pieces before trying a new drill on exposed areas. The drill usually cuts best if it is kept accurately at right angles to the tile surface.

Because the structure of the bath enclosure itself prohibits any movement of the frame from left to right, about all you have to worry about is something that will stay stuck in the wall to prohibit fore and aft shifting. Anchor plugs came with the enclosure shown in the photos. They have a soft lead core and a fiber outer wrapping. You have to be rather careful in starting screws in them. If the hole in the wall is just a little too big, the plug tends to disappear into the wall when the screw is pushed in. It is wise to start with a small drill and to work upward until you find the right size for your particular plugs. The fit should be just a little on the snug side, and the plugs should require very gentle tapping to make them enter.

It is very difficult to cut the panels so that the openings match perfectly with the soap dish, toilet paper holder, toothbrush rack, etc. It's less trouble to make the openings a trifle larger than necessary and to finish off with simple molding. Ordinary flat aluminum stock ½ in. wide and ⅛ in. thick proved fine for the purpose. The corners were mitered with a hack saw. To provide a good "tooth" for the mounting cement, the back surface of the molding and the meeting surface of the wall paneling were sanded lightly. Contact cement holds the strips firmly in place. The joint cracks were filled with aluminum plastic cement, and then sanded and steel-wooled to a bright, smooth finish.

—*Emil E. Brodbeck* •

It costs less if you can find space for an added bathroom within the present structure of your house. The next best arrangement to add space is to enclose all or part of a porch, as is being done here, above.

NOW YOU CAN . . .

add a bathroom

IF YOU CAN FIND a place for added bathroom facilities without building an addition to your house, the cost will be far less. If you can't find space within the existing structure, perhaps you can enclose all or part of a porch.

If there is no other choice, and you have to build an addition to gain the space needed, keep in mind that the room you add need not be the bathroom. It may work out better in your house plan to add a new bathroom, or some other room, and convert some part of your existing space to the bathroom. Here's why: The closer you are to existing pipes, the lower will be your costs. Further, the closer you are to existing plumbing, the easier it will be to hide pipes.

Where to Put a Bath. You can squeeze a full bath in a space as small as 54x78 inches. You can often get this much space by removing the wall in back-to-back closets. The untraveled end of a hall may

have 30 or more square feet, and if it does, it can serve. You may be able to find the space under a stairway, or under the eaves in an attic. If the headroom is low, you may have to dispense with a shower, but you can still have a tub.

You can convert a pantry or a laundry. In the pantry, you still may be able to preserve much of the storage space by means of a storage wall. In converting a laundry, by use of modern appliances, there still may be space for clothes washing. You can either get a combination washer-dryer, or stack the dryer over the washer.

You can divide an existing large bath into two bathrooms, or at least into 1½ baths. Since the tub is the least used of the three fixtures, it could be shared between the two new rooms.

A half bath (lavatory and toilet) requires only 30x60 inches. You can fit one into a walk-in closet. A toilet and shower can be accommodated in a 3-foot wide slice

Use a skylight to bring natural daylight to an inside bathroom. Drop the level of the ceiling down to accommodate pipes overhead. A new ceiling of acoustical tile is quick, easy to install.

Every bathroom needs one or more ventilators to expel vapor, odors, and bring in fresh air. A squirrel-cage type is best for handling large quantities of air quickly, with minimum sound.

Lowering ceiling makes bathroom cozier, easier to heat. Acoustical tiles will provide both sound and thermal insulation. Tile, at right, is being marked for cut around NuTone heater unit outlet.

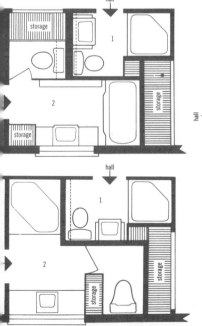

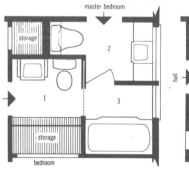

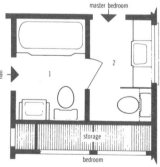

Here are four ways to lay out multiple bathroom facilities. By compacting the arrangements, several members of a family can make use of the rooms at one time. There is also the plumbing aspect to consider: Short lines will save money!

American-Standard

319

taken off the end of a bedroom, a space 36x96 inches being ample. You may even find that you have enough space for all three fixtures if you put the toilet at one end of the slice, the shower at the other, and the washbasin opposite the door at the middle. Some small washbasins are only 12 inches deep. If you are cramped for space, get a toilet that is smaller than standard. Shower stalls are commonly 30x30 inches.

The Inside Bathroom. Don't dismiss space as unusable just because it has no window. An inside bathroom, in many ways, is superior to one that has an exterior wall.

It is warmer. It is less drafty. It doesn't have the problem of condensation on windows. It is more private. It is quieter. With a good fan, its ventilation is superior. The fan should be connected so that it comes on with the light and has enough capacity to change air completely every 5 minutes. Put a grill in the lower part of the door or wall for incoming air, or take a slice off the bottom of the door.

If you want natural daylight in an inside

Snap a chalk line down center of bathroom's main area, and begin installation of cork floor tiles here. Though the felt is put down with linoleum paste, waterproof cement is required for tiles.

New plastic drawers are easy to install, have steel runners, glide on smooth nylon pads. Any style front to match cabinet can be attached to drawer fronts. Plastic can never warp or stick.

bathroom, you may also be able to arrange that with a skylight. The skylight can include a ventilator built into its curb. It may also serve as a lighting fixture, so that round-the-clock light comes from the one source.

Structural Considerations. A bathroom and its equipment may add considerable weight to your house. You aren't likely to encounter any difficulties in this regard unless your floors are already sagging and shaky, or if you have to do some heavy notching of joists to accommodate plumbing pipes. Here's how you can save on weight: Apply ceramic tile with adhesive

FIXTURE SIZES

BATHTUB:	Width: Height: Length:	Usually 31", but may be 30" or 32". 14" to 16" Usually 54" or 60", but may also be 42" or 66". Square tubs are approximately 48" on a side.
TOILET:	Width: Height: Depth: Clearance:	Most tanks are 22½", but range is from 20" to 24". Usually 30". Range is from 18½" to 40". Usually 30" from front of bowl to back of tank, but range is from 26" to 32". Need a minimum access of 18" x 30" at front. Also allow 30" for tank to give it some clearance on each side.
LAVATORY	Width: Depth: Height: Clearance:	Usual is 24", but may range from 12" to 36". 12" to 24" with 18" most popular. Corner style measures 12" to 19" on a side. 31" is standard, but 34" to 36" is best when unit is for adult use only. Requires minimum access space of 18" x 24" at front.

Allow waterproof cement to dry five minutes before setting tile firmly in place over it. Use care to keep the cement off the tiles. Accidental smears can be wiped away very easily with a soapy rag.

Provide as much storage as you can in the bathroom. You can store not only toilet articles and linen here, but clothing as well. Corner storage cabinet needs to have room on only one side wall.

Cabinet has 4 different sizes of drawers below upper section of adjustable shelves. Unit is suspended off the floor to match the style of the adjoining off-the-floor vanity-lavatory as shown.

By attaching metal shelf standards for support of shelves, the placement of the shelves becomes completely flexible. Shelves are of plywood trimmed along front edge with thin wood strip.

instead of mortar. Use plastic wall, counter, and floor finishes. Use a steel tub and lavatory; they are lighter than cast iron.

In building storage, use new lightweight plastic drawers, such as those made by Washington Steel Products, Tacoma 1, Washington, and available at hardware and lumber dealers. They are not only feather light, but, made of high-impact polystyrene, are as rugged as they come.

If reinforcement of structure is essential, support first-floor joists by running a 4x10 beam as support under their center line. Second floor joists can be reinforced by spiking extra joists to existing ones. Ends of

these new joists should rest on bearing partitions. Sure, this does require opening up floor or ceiling, but you'll probably be doing that anyway for installation of pipes. Or if you drop the ceiling level in the floor below to give space for pipes, the extra supporting members can be installed here.

If your ceiling height is 8 feet or more, you'll also find definite advantages in dropping the bathroom ceiling to 7 feet. You can run pipes through the space, and the dead air pocket created will make the room both warmer and quieter. A new ceiling of acoustical tile, such as those made by Armstrong, is easy to install, inexpensive. •

Building a Bay Window

by George Daniels

It's easy and inexpensive if you plan the job carefully

IF YOU'D like a brighter living room with the feeling of much greater space, and you'd like it on a small budget, the chances are a bay window is your answer. In a typical small home it can add enough space to keep dining area from crowding living room, and its large room-brightening glass area creates the impression of a considerably larger room. Yet, unlike a major room extension it doesn't require a costly pile of materials nor a lengthy construction job. And the room to which it is added can remain in use during the work.

Check on the practical factors before you decide on the size or location of your bay window. For a first step, look in your basement to see if any major plumbing (like drain or soil pipes) runs through the wall area you want to open up. If so, get an estimate from your plumber on shifting the pipes. This can be a big cost-booster and may not even be practical. Your best bet in that event is another window location.

If the window is to be in a nonsupporting wall, the job will be a little simpler as a heavy header across the top of the wall

Photos here show house with and without bay window. Bay window replaces four lower windows, as photo shows. Addition brightens living room, adds about 4 feet to length.

First step is to dig trench below frost line for concrete footing of bay window foundation. Small opening is made through house wall to assure accurate matching of floor level of room and window. You can buy concrete you'll need by cubic yard.

No form is needed for footing. Ready-mix truck delivers concrete, chutes it into trench. Like water in trough, wet concrete tends to level itself, but must be checked with mason's level, trowled to flat upper surface, ready for masonry's blocks.

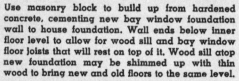

Use masonry block to build up from hardened concrete, cementing new bay window foundation wall to house foundation. Wall ends below inner floor level to allow for wood sill and bay window floor joists that will rest on top of it. Wood sill atop new foundation may be shimmed up with thin wood to bring new and old floors to the same level.

Wood sill and plywood subfloor are installed. Outside wall surface (siding and sheathing) have been cut away below windows, exposing inside wall. Bottom of inside wall has also been opened for 1 or 2 inches above floor level to permit new window subfloor to be slipped, nailed into place. Bay window floor joists run across new foundation.

opening won't be needed, and the room ceiling may be continued smoothly into the bay window area. If you're opening a supporting wall, you'll need a larger header or girder across the top of the opening to support the portion of the floor above that which was previously supported by the wall. This isn't much added expense but it usually calls for a visible beam (which can be made decorative) or a lower ceiling level in the bay window.

An easy way to tell one type wall from the other: a nonsupporting wall runs parallel to the joists or beams in the floor above. You can check in the attic or even in the basement, as joists in upper and lower floors usually run in the same direction. Outside walls that run at right angles to the floor joists above them are supporting walls.

Exposure and view are the other major location factors. Naturally, you'll favor the best-view location if practicable, though shrubbery may be used when practical considerations make a less favorable location necessary. As to exposure, favor north or east if summer heat is a major problem. If it isn't, a bay window facing west will

brighten your living room at cocktail time and even through dinner on summer evenings. In cool climates a window to the south affords the greatest overall sunlight throughout the day. A shade tree in line with it is an ideal combination, as summer foliage blocks direct sun in hot weather; bare branches let it pass in winter.

If you plan to build your own bay window, you'll save work by planning it with a rectangular floor plan. If you're set on the traditional angular form, however, a portable circular saw like the one shown in the photos, will minimize the extra work of angle cutting on rafters and other framing parts.

To keep costs down, plan your job around standard window sizes. For sake of appearance be sure that the muntins and sash parts (particularly along horizontal lines) of adjacent windows align.

You can assure weathertightness and maximum strength by using plyscore for sheathing, subfloor, and roof, while cutting labor on these parts to a minimum. Because of the large glass area, three or four standard 4x8 panels are enough for a moderate sized bay window.

Here is typical framing around a small window in conventional house wall. Note arrangement of uprights at window ends to support header beam. at top of window, which, in turn, supports short uprights from the top of window to top of wall.

To enlarge wall opening for bay window installation, framing is altered like this. Horizontal "sill" piece across opening has been removed to let floor run through it. Large header beam across top of opening provides support for floor above, previously supported by intermediate uprights or studs. This is necessary when opening is made in "supporting" wall. If it's non-supporting wall header can usually be omitted, giving full ceiling height in the bay window.

Here's how hip-type angled roof framing is laid out. Rear members are nailed to existing house wall. Only one ceiling joist is shown (center) in bay window framing. Finished structure should have them on 16-inch centers, the same as in the house.

Simplest type of bay window roof framing is possible if bay window is rectangular in form, like the one shown here. Saves work, material.

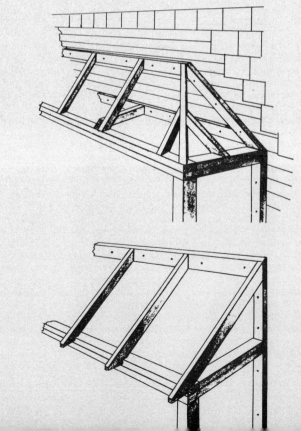

Wall framing now goes up. House siding (shingles) are removed 2 feet above bay window framing to nail new framing directly to house sheathing and framing. Roof of bay window starts about a foot above top of framing shown here, and slopes down.

The windows are now fitted carefully, and trim is installed, as shown in photograph above. Plank temporarily closes opening along bottom of inner wall at floor level. Living room is still usable as work progresses. Cloth could cover work area.

The large glass area leaves little interior wall area not covered by trim. In a typical installation this means few, if any, wall-board joints to spackle except at corners, where the job's easy even for an amateur. The small wall area also lets you use the best grade of insulation between walls without much increase in cost. Usually the ceiling can be covered with a single wall-board panel, requiring only a single seam to spackle at the bay window-room juncture.

To eliminate the need for a time-consuming finishing job on the finish flooring in the bay window area buy it prefinished. As you'd need to buy the finishing materials, in addition to unfinished flooring, the difference in overall cost is slight, the saving in time and work is great. And you're assured of a professional appearance.

Most of the bay window framing consists of stock 2x4's, even for roof rafters, as the span is seldom more than four or five feet. The joists that support the floor, however, should in most instances be the same size

as those in the adjoining house floor. Although lighter joists would usually be more than adequate, you'll save trouble by matching them to the house joists size, as you'll find it much easier to bring floor levels flush with each other. Simply build the bay window foundation up to the same height as the house foundation and use the same type of sill and joists. Usually it will be easier to run the bay window floor joists parallel to the house wall, with ends supported on the new foundation, even though the span might be a little shorter if they ran inward to the house.

For a first-hand look at the construction details that will go into your bay window have a look at the sill atop the foundation walls in your basement and the roof rafters in your attic, assuming you haven't done an interior finishing job in these areas of your house. The next best bet: look over any new home construction job in the framing stage. You'll see that you can do the work with ordinary hand tools, though a power saw will speed the job on the more elaborate designs.

Windows are now permanently installed, new siding shingles are on house and bay window. They will be stained to match rest of house. Metal flashing is installed under lowest course of shingles above bay window roof, and led out over start of roofing to prevent rain seepage at juncture. Now that bay window is completely weathertight, inner wall separating it from living room wall is removed. Header at top of opening through wall had been installed previously. Finished window adds distinction to house.

If you need help in visualizing your basic design use large sheets of wrapping paper Scotch-taped together to permit a full-sized pencil outline of your floor plan, or use several joined strips of building paper like Tanskin for the same purpose. You can pencil in the location of studs, based on the window sizes you plan to use, and work out the rest of your framing from there. You can choose the window sizes from a wide selection at your lumber-yard, and get standard ready-made screens and storm windows to match if you want them.

If you're casually handy with tools, the job on an average sized bay window shouldn't take more than two weekends of spare time, and you won't have to open your existing house wall until the bay window unit has been made weathertight. •

cantilevered CHILD'S BED

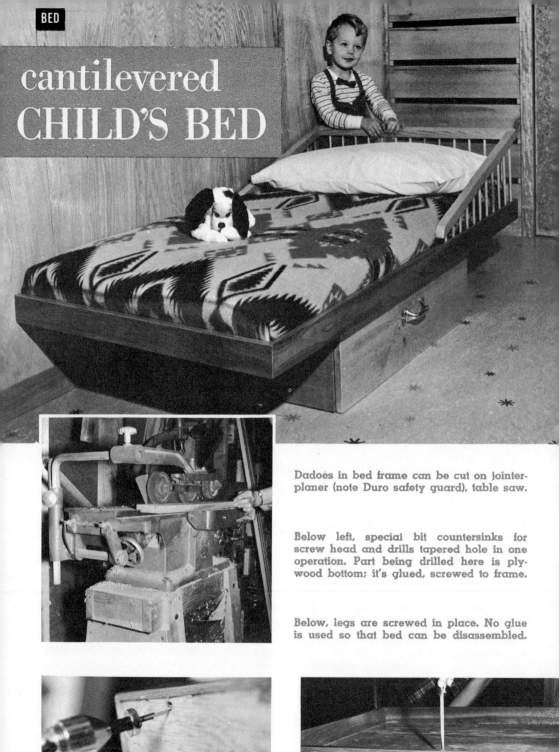

Dadoes in bed frame can be cut on jointer-planer (note Duro safety guard), table saw.

Below left, special bit countersinks for screw head and drills tapered hole in one operation. Part being drilled here is plywood bottom; it's glued, screwed to frame.

Below, legs are screwed in place. No glue is used so that bed can be disassembled.

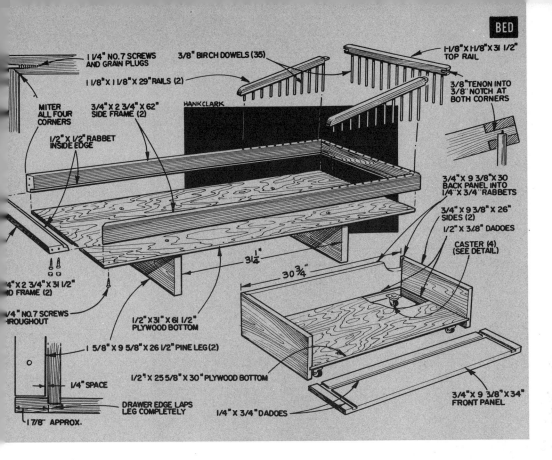

1 1/4" NO.7 SCREWS AND GRAIN PLUGS

3/8" BIRCH DOWELS (35)

1 1/8"X 1 1/8"X 31 1/2" TOP RAIL

1 1/8"X 1 1/8"X 29"RAILS (2)

3/8" TENON INTO 3/8" NOTCH AT BOTH CORNERS

MITER ALL FOUR CORNERS

3/4"X 2 3/4"X 62" SIDE FRAME (2)

HANK CLARK

1/2"X 1/2"RABBET INSIDE EDGE

3/4"X 9 3/8"X 30 BACK PANEL INTO 1/4"X 3/4" RABBETS

3/4"X 9 3/8"X 26" SIDES (2)

1/2"X 3/8" DADOES

CASTER (4) (SEE DETAIL.)

3 1/4"

30 3/4"

4"X 2 3/4"X 31 1/2" D FRAME (2)

1/4"NO.7 SCREWS 1ROUGHOUT

1/2"X31"X 61 1/2" PLYWOOD BOTTOM

1 5/8"X 9 5/8"X 26 1/2" PINE LEG (2)

1/2"X 25 5/8"X 30" PLYWOOD BOTTOM

1/4" SPACE

DRAWER EDGE LAPS LEG COMPLETELY

1/4"X 3/4"DADOES

3/4"X 9 3/8"X34" FRONT PANEL

1 7/8" APPROX.

Simple, modern, this bed also provides toy or storage space.

By Harold Kelly

SIMPLE construction, modern styling and a sturdy result are the virtues of this bed. And just as important is the storage drawer built in underneath, easy to pull out for use as a toy chest. The bed shown here is 5 feet long, for a 3-year-old, but the author also built a full-size one for his oldest child; in that one the drawer serves for blanket storage.

Construction took less than 8 hours, and cost can be as low as $10, without mattress. The frame is solid cherry, head rail is ash, bed and drawer bottom are 1/2-in. plywood, drawer sides are 3/4-in. thick pine, bed legs are simply fir 2x10's.

The 3/4x2 3/4-in. cherry frame has a 1/2-in. dado cut in the bottom edge to receive the plywood bottom. The corners are cut at a 45-degree angle and glued and screwed together, using two 1 1/4-in. No. 7 screws at each corner (same size screws are used throughout project).

Cut the legs to size and screw them in place. These 2x10's can be bought at a local lumberyard—but note that they actually will measure 1 5/8x9 5/8 in. Cut the drawer sides from 3/4x10-in. shelving (which will also measure 9 5/8 in. wide). Reduce this width to 9 3/8 in. to afford sufficient clearance for the drawer to roll in and out without binding. Buy the rollers that are to be screwed to the drawer bottom before you cut dadoes in the drawer sides. Reason is that the rollers should protrude about 1/8 in. below the bottom of the drawer sides, and roller sizes vary; therefore you'll have to locate the drawer bottom to suit. The free-rolling casters used here cost 15c apiece. A simple brass door handle was used for the drawer.

The headboard is designed so that there are no sharp corners for the child to roll into while tossing in his sleep.

Headboard rails are bored to receive the ⅜-in. thick birch dowels at proper angle.

Here, back of headboard rail is drilled. Without drill press, make jig to get angle.

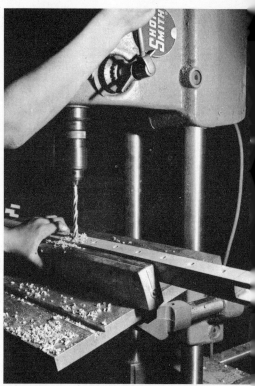

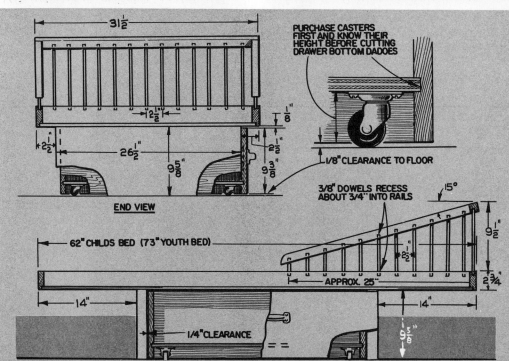

END VIEW

31½

12½

1/8"

2½"

26½"

9⅝"

2½"

9⅜"

PURCHASE CASTERS FIRST AND KNOW THEIR HEIGHT BEFORE CUTTING DRAWER BOTTOM DADOES

1/8" CLEARANCE TO FLOOR

3/8" DOWELS RECESS ABOUT 3/4" INTO RAILS

15°

62" CHILDS BED (73" YOUTH BED)

9½"

2½"

APPROX. 25"

2¾"

14"

1/4" CLEARANCE

14"

9⅝"

Birch dowels are spaced 2½ in. on centers and marked off on frame before holes are drilled. Hole in side of jig is used to space the holes evenly. Headboard is all assembled at this point.

Dowels on headboard are aligned with holes in frame. Then merely force-fit the dowels in place, without use of glue. Use scrap block under hammer to avoid mark.

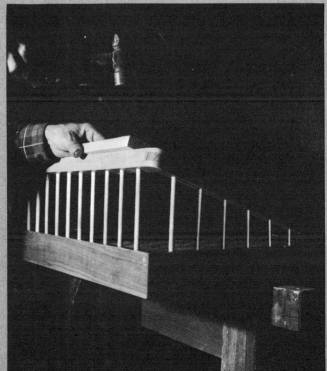

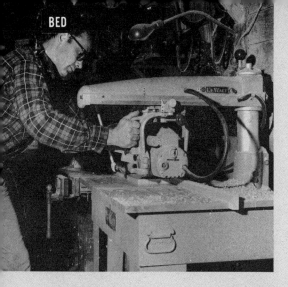

Drawer sides are cut and dadoed with table saw—preferably with overhead radial saw.

Drawer bottom is positioned so that rollers protrude ⅛ in. below drawer sides.

The head rail is made of 1¼x1¼-in. ash, but only because it was on hand—cherry, oak or any hardwood will do as well. Refer to the drawings on preceding pages for the proper size and angle of the head rail.

The ⅜-in. birch dowels were spaced 2½ in. on centers. The holes are drilled in the head rail after it is cut to size and assembled—a drill press is real handy for getting the angles just right. If you don't have a drill press, the same type of jig that was used to help drill the holes in the bed frame (see photo) can be used with the head rail. Dowels are

fitted into the head rail and then trimmed to size.

Finally, the headboard unit is fitted into the bed frame and forced into place. For a finish, the whole unit was given three coats of Fabulon, smoothed down with steel wool between coats. If you don't care to make your own foam-rubber mattress, one can be bought for around $38, complete with zippered cover. Foam rubber is a good bet, since a good grade will assure you of no sag in the middle or the usual mattress troubles due to the young one jumping in bed. •

Toy-or-storage drawer slides out easily, contributes to a neat, clutter-free bedroom.

Whole bed gets three coats of Fabulon for the hard and durable finish necessary on children's furniture. Steel wool between coats and, for modern dull finish, after final coat. Fabulon dries dust-free in a few minutes.

FABULON

THE
fabulous
FLOOR FINISH

BEDROOM STORAGE WALL

Winter or summer, all your storage problems will be

eliminated if you build this functional wall unit.

By David X. Manners

TO get the most storage in the least space, build this "storage wall." A built-in gives a feeling of spaciousness to a room for it eliminates need for separate items of furniture such as wardrobes, chests, and chiffoniers and the inevitable waste of space between them. In either new construction or remodeling, a storage wall will cost you much less than the equivalent in furniture.

Maybe you think of these units as rather drab, painted affairs. They needn't be: new prefinished hardwood plywood panels and contact bond cement make it easy to give your built-in a fine-furniture look without a fine-furniture price tag.

The storage wall has other advan-

tages. Unlike a door in a wall closet, the full-front opening of its hanging section means easy accessibility to all clothing. Its smooth-operating bifolding doors eliminate the need for doorswing space. You don't have to run finish flooring or carpeting under it, a not inconsequential saving.

Both height and width of the unit are variable. Usually, the best plan is to run it the entire length of the wall, eliminating the need for separate ends. The top of the wall may be kept in line with doors and windows or it may be run all the way to the ceiling. The highest shelf the average woman can reach without standing on a chair is six feet, so keep the total height of the wall to no more

SUPPORTS for floor of unit are spaced to fall under partition walls. If floor is uneven, use shingle scraps for leveling.

SHORT cleat, nailed against the 1x3 kickboard, is used to stiffen it under drawer sections. Shelving acts as closet floor.

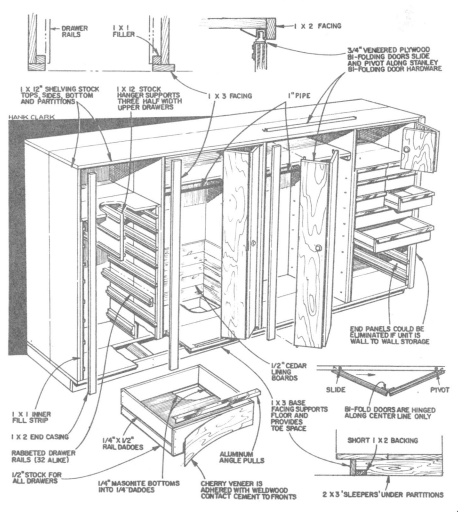

DRAWER RAILS

I X I FILLER

I X 2 FACING

3/4" VENEERED PLYWOOD BI-FOLDING DOORS SLIDE AND PIVOT ALONG STANLEY BI-FOLDING DOOR HARDWARE

I X 12" SHELVING STOCK TOPS, SIDES, BOTTOM AND PARTITIONS

I X 12 STOCK HANGER SUPPORTS THREE HALF WIDTH UPPER DRAWERS

I X 3 FACING

I" PIPE

HANK CLARK

END PANELS COULD BE ELIMINATED IF UNIT IS WALL TO WALL STORAGE

1/2" CEDAR LINING BOARDS

SLIDE

PIVOT

I X I INNER FILL STRIP

I X 2 END CASING

RABBETED DRAWER RAILS (32 ALIKE)

1/2" STOCK FOR ALL DRAWERS

1/4" X 1/2" RAIL DADOES

1/4" MASONITE BOTTOMS INTO 1/4"DADOES

ALUMINUM ANGLE PULLS

CHERRY VENEER IS ADHERED WITH WELDWOOD CONTACT CEMENT TO FRONTS

I X 3 BASE FACING SUPPORTS FLOOR AND PROVIDES TOE SPACE

BI-FOLD DOORS ARE HINGED ALONG CENTER LINE ONLY

SHORT I X 2 BACKING

2 X 3 'SLEEPERS' UNDER PARTITIONS

PARTITIONS are made of two 1x12-inch boards, held together with corrugated fasteners; ¾-inch plywood may also be used.

OUT-OF-PLUMB walls, above, call for the use of a scriber to mark the boards so that they may be trimmed down for perfect fit.

CLOSET top, left, is supported at the ends by a 1x1½-inch cleat. Top, like floor, is constructed of two 1x12-inch shelving boards.

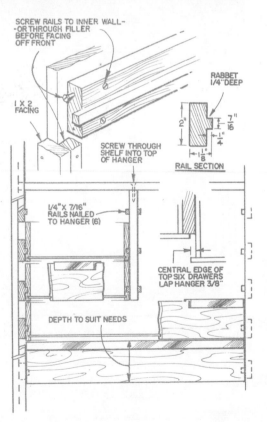

SCREW RAILS TO INNER WALL—OR THROUGH FILLER BEFORE FACING OFF FRONT

RABBET ¼" DEEP

1 X 2 FACING

SCREW THROUGH SHELF INTO TOP OF HANGER

2" 7/16" ¼" ⅛"

RAIL SECTION

¼" X 7/16" RAILS NAILED TO HANGER (6)

CENTRAL EDGE OF TOP SIX DRAWERS LAP HANGER ⅜"

DEPTH TO SUIT NEEDS

than seven feet if it is to be used only for storing items in regular use. Space higher than that may be used for dead storage or items used infrequently.

In planing your project bear in mind the efficient use of materials. Try to arrange the bi-folding and cabinet doors so they'll be a size that will come out of standard panels with a minimum of waste. In the unit shown, the ¾-inch doors came out of one 4x8 and one 4x6-foot panel with just enough left over for trim pieces.

Make the depth of the unit 24 inches, exclusive of the doors. A depth less than that won't take hanging garments without crowding and may interfere with the operation of the doors. A depth greater than 26 inches is wasteful of space.

Don't run any drawers higher than you can look into—about 52 inches. For most efficient storage, keep drawers as shallow as possible, matching them to items to be stored. You can make good drawer slides of wood, but for really easy-rolling drawers, or where they have to support heavy loads, get metal rolling drawer slides. Slides should be

AT FRONT of each partition, and at both ends of closet, a 1x2 is attached, with 1x1 strips filling in along the top and bottom.

SMALL woodworking vise is helpful to hold drawer parts when nailing together with cement-coated nails. Drawers are precut.

BOTTOMS of drawers are made from ½-inch tempered Masonite. Planing edges makes them slide easily into the ¼-inch grooves.

BRACES keep partitions in line as each drawer is individually fitted and the runners for the drawers above are installed.

DIVIDER with 7/16x¾-inch track strips is screwed to the support. It will contain a double bank of narrower-width drawers.

CEDAR lining installation is begun at the rear of closet. Start each row with cut-off piece from previous board, as shown.

HAT SHELF above hanging section is made of cedar board; install it 9 inches from top. Shelving is finished before installation.

the same length as the drawers; but for greater drawer extension (and if space permits), get longer slides and allow them to extend behind the drawers.

Lining the hanging section with cedar won't discourage moths, but the wood has an incomparable fragrance and eliminates the need for painting or other finish. To achieve the "furniture look," drawer fronts and trim in the unit shown are of prefinished Weldwood cherry plywood. Doors are of birch, for which a special cherry stain is available, if desired. (Roddiscraft cherry for birch.)

Drawer pulls are made of brass angle stock, but aluminum may be used, either natural or painted. Finish and hardware should be matched to your own decorative scheme.

If the storage wall is run to the ceiling, a dead storage section can easily be added above the unit shown by using Reynolds aluminum sliding door track and sliding panels of Masonite Presdwood, Peg-board, plywood, or a decorative plastic such as Wasco Acrylite. This plastic is available with colorful embedments of leaves, ferns, fabric, even butterflies. Also worth considering are new plastic-coated Marlite panels in woodgrain, marble, and color finishes.

The base of the unit is made of 2x3's, 21 inches long. The floor resting on these supports is 1x12-inch shelving. Since these boards actually measure only 11½ inches wide, nail a 1-inch strip along the edge of the board that fits against the wall. This will give a full 24-inch depth inside the doors. The finished storage unit will overhang the base by approximately 3¼ inches. •

CLOTHES rod is 1-inch pipe. A nail through the end of pipe will keep it in position after it is inserted into the wall holes.

DRAWER pulls may be made of 1x1-inch brass or Reynolds aluminum angle. Cost is less than for lots of standard hardware.

BIFOLDING door track is made by Stanley. Mark track to length for cutting and install it above the hanging clothes section.

DOORS pivot at top and bottom on adjustable nylon guides. Follow the manufacturer's instruction when installing them.

HINGE leaf, above right, spaces the folding doors slightly apart at joint. Light tap on a nail insures easy starting of the screws.

CASING, right, covers crack at pivot ends of doors. Trim is also used above and below doors to conceal hardware. Below, the finished storage wall blends in handsomely with decor of a bedroom, den or hallway.

A Child's Bedroom

A complete suite for the youngsters, with a place for everything.

ALTHOUGH these units were actually made to completely furnish a young fellow's room, without having to lay out money for ready-made pieces, the designs are such that the young people will find them practical way up into their teens. And many a grown-up will find his room made more livable by units such as this, modified to suit his tastes and pursuits.

A room does not have to be large to have so many built-ins. The sample floor plan shown is for a bedroom no more than 10x10 feet. All the projects are dimensioned to suit this size room. So if the room you have in mind is this size—give or take a foot in either direction—you can work right from the plans provided. The work top, of course, can be as long as needed or there is room for. Some cabinets can be added underneath this to provide drawer space close to the work-top, or possibly a shallow drawer to hold the writing tools needed at a desk.

Before you start construction, make your own floor plan—a very simple one, but drawing it to scale. Then make scaled cut-outs of the projects shown here and place them on the layout, moving them about until you have arrived at an arrangement that makes the most of available space and which provides as much open area as possible. Traffic patterns in a bedroom are not critical but don't neglect enough room around a bed so friend wife won't have to struggle to prepare it, and enough room in front of the work-top or desk so a chair can be placed there.

If possible, arrange the work area to get light from an existing window. Leave the most open floor space near the entrance door. Don't place projects so doors opening into the room will bang into them. Remember that built-ins become part of the house and you can't take them with you when you go. If this idea doesn't appeal to you, make the projects as units that can be moved around and do not attach to walls.

Wardrobe

Start this off by cutting the three main, vertical panels to overall size and notching them at the base for the toe space. Follow with the floor frames (B and C) and the ceiling frames (E and F). Erect one panel, set in one floor frame (which can be assembled as a separate unit). Then follow with the second panel, the second floor frame and then the last panel. Floor frames can be nailed to the floor; the panels to the frames. Add the ceiling frames, driving a few nails through them into the ceiling joists if possible.

When erecting these three panels, work with a level and a square to be sure the panels are plumb and perfectly parallel to each other. This will pay off later when it comes to hanging doors and fitting in drawer fronts.

Next, install all your shelves. Make and install the drawer frames. Install these very carefully so that all the drawer parts (drawers are identical) can be cut on a production basis. In fact, it wouldn't be a bad idea to make a spacer block having the same dimensions as a drawer front, and use it to space the drawer frames correctly;

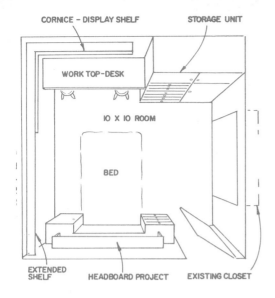

CORNICE – DISPLAY SHELF   STORAGE UNIT

WORK TOP-DESK

10 X 10 ROOM

BED

EXTENDED SHELF   HEADBOARD PROJECT   EXISTING CLOSET

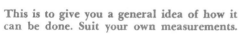

This is to give you a general idea of how it can be done. Suit your own measurements.

Keep in mind that every inch of space should be utilized, even the shelf over the cornice.

341

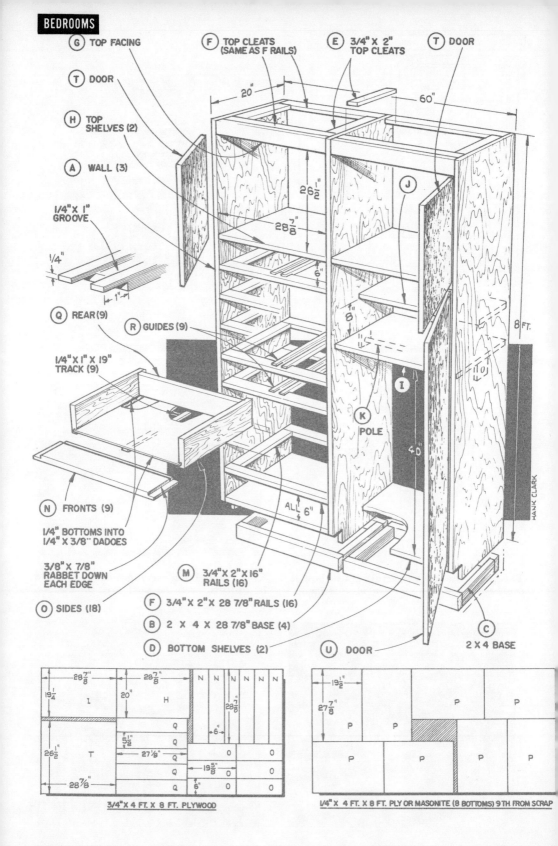

G TOP FACING

F TOP CLEATS (SAME AS F RAILS)

E 3/4" X 2" TOP CLEATS

T DOOR

T DOOR

H TOP SHELVES (2)

A WALL (3)

1/4" X 1" GROOVE

1/4"

1"

Q REAR (9)

R GUIDES (9)

1/4" X 1" X 19" TRACK (9)

N FRONTS (9)

1/4" BOTTOMS INTO 1/4" X 3/8" DADOES

3/8" X 7/8" RABBET DOWN EACH EDGE

O SIDES (18)

M 3/4" X 2" X 16" RAILS (16)

F 3/4" X 2" X 28 7/8" RAILS (16)

B 2 X 4 X 28 7/8" BASE (4)

D BOTTOM SHELVES (2)

U DOOR

J

K POLE

I

C 2 X 4 BASE

20"

60"

26 1/2"

28 7/8"

6"

8"

40"

ALL 6"

8 FT.

HANK CLARK

3/4" X 4 FT. X 8 FT. PLYWOOD

28 7/8" | 28 7/8"
19 1/4" | I | 20" | H | N N N N N N
26 1/2" | T | 5 1/2" | Q | 28 7/8"
| 27 7/8" | Q | 6"
28 7/8" | Q | 19 5/8" | O O
| Q | 6" | O O

1/4" X 4 FT. X 8 FT. PLY OR MASONITE (8 BOTTOMS) 9TH FROM SCRAP

19 1/2"
27 7/8"
P P P P P P P P P P

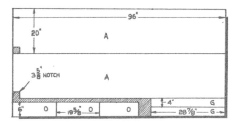

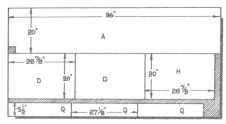

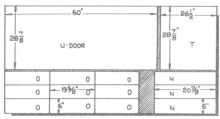

ALL THREE PANELS ARE 3/4" X 4 FT. X 8 FT. PLYWOOD

starting with the bottom one and using the spacer to position each succeeding frame. Frames can be held in place by nails driven into them through the vertical panels. Coat the edges of the frames with glue before nailing them. Another method of installing the frames and shelves would be to set them in dadoes. These would have to be cut in the vertical panels before they are erected, and dimensions controlling the width of the shelves and frames would have to be adjusted if the overall size suggested for the project is to be maintained. For example; if the dadoes are 3/8 inch deep then the width of frames and shelves must be increased by 3/4 inch. Glue and finishing nails would still be used to install them.

Make the drawers by starting with the front, cutting it to size and checking it against the opening it must fit. When one is right cut the remainder to that same size. Follow with the drawer sides—cut dadoes for the drawer bottom in sides and front. Assemble these four pieces, then add the back.

Cut the doors to provide about $\frac{1}{32}$-inch clearance on all but the hinge sides and install them with 2-inch butt hinges.

Headboard Project

Start this one by making the two

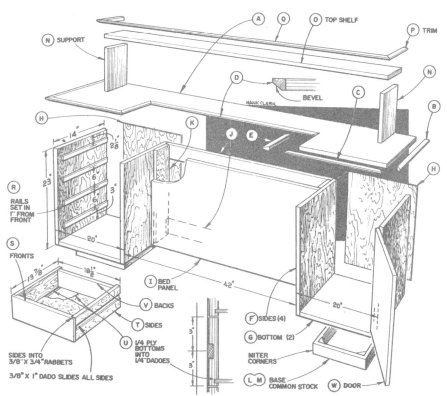

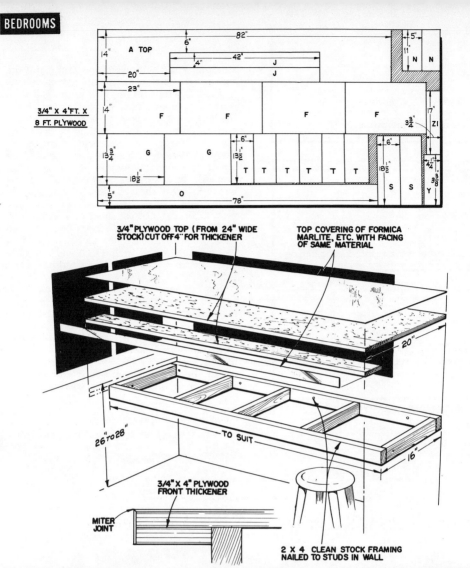

3/4" X 4' FT. X 8 FT. PLYWOOD

3/4" PLYWOOD TOP (FROM 24" WIDE STOCK) CUT OFF 4" FOR THICKENER

TOP COVERING OF FORMICA MARLITE, ETC. WITH FACING OF SAME MATERIAL

3/4" X 4" PLYWOOD FRONT THICKENER

MITER JOINT

2 X 4 CLEAN STOCK FRAMING NAILED TO STUDS IN WALL

"boxes"; one of which holds the four drawers, the other being a small cabinet. These are open at the top for the top of unit (A) will provide sufficient rigidity after it is added to the structure. It's a good idea, before assembling the drawer enclosure, to lay out carefully the positions of the drawer slides. These should be cut to exact dimensions and smoothly sanded to ride easily in the dadoes cut in the drawer sides. When you're sure they are in correct position, coat the back edge with glue and install them with small, countersunk screws. Be sure the screws are driven in far enough to be slightly under the surface of the wood so they won't interfere with drawer movement.

Assemble the box-feet (L and M) as separate units, toenailing the glue blocks in place after coating all mating surfaces liberally with glue. Attach these to the units by nailing down into them through the base of the units.

The separator (made from parts I, J and K) is also assembled separately, then installed between the two end units with screws. It isn't necessary to use glue here.

Make the top very carefully, laying it out first on the plywood, and checking before cutting to be sure dimensions are correct.

The trim strips which edge the top of the unit and the shelf are beveled on the forward edge to gentle the appearance of the horizontal pieces. Although the bill-of-materials lists these trim strips as individual pieces, it's good practice to run this bevel on long pieces of material and to get

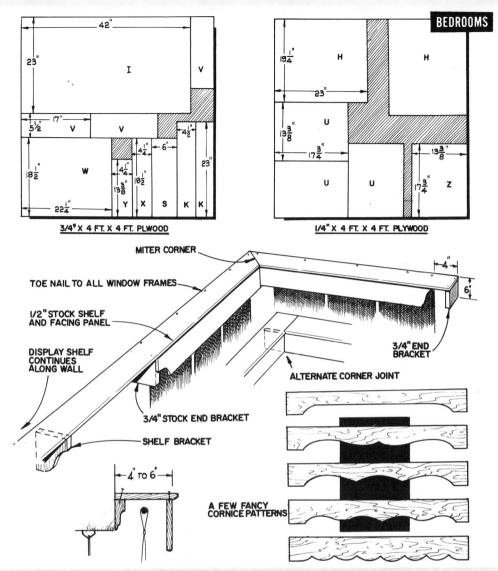

3/4" X 4 FT. X 4 FT. PLWOOD

1/4" X 4 FT. X 4 FT. PLYWOOD

MITER CORNER

TOE NAIL TO ALL WINDOW FRAMES

1/2" STOCK SHELF AND FACING PANEL

DISPLAY SHELF CONTINUES ALONG WALL

3/4" STOCK END BRACKET

SHELF BRACKET

3/4" END BRACKET

ALTERNATE CORNER JOINT

A FEW FANCY CORNICE PATTERNS

them completely shaped and sanded before sizing them. Even then, it will be more convenient to cut pieces to size as you go along, checking them on the part. Cut and fit all miters very carefully for these are most important on final appearance. Attach trim strips with glue and 2-inch finishing nails.

The two verticals which support the shelf are nailed to the shelf, but are not permanently attached to the headboard unit.

Work Counter or Desk

This is merely a 2x4 frame topped with a sheet of plywood which is in turn covered with the finishing material. If the ends and back can be rigidly attached, in this case —one end to a wall, the other to the wardrobe unit and the back to a wall—the counter can be quite long without requiring vertical supports (legs). It's best to install the frame and the plywood cover and the strip which builds up the front edge completely first. Then carefully add the Formica, using contact cement.

Cornice and Display Shelf

The cornice and shelf add the final touch to the room. Design here can definitely identify the room as being a child's or a teen-ager's, or a grown-up's. If you want to remain neutral, use a simple design. A plain cornice can be decorated (after painting) with decals. A youngster will be delighted if you decorate the cornice with overlaid, nursery-rhyme cutouts made on a jig saw and colorfully painted. • *By R. J. DeCristoforo*

345

Music Bench

Give the teen-ager a private nook

for relaxation and music enjoyment

Students can't keep their noses to the grindstone all the time. Sometimes they have to put their ears to the turntable.

For that music break, here's a music bench with a place for records, record player, and a seat to relax on while listening. It's a break for the well organized teen-ager's room, too, because it keeps the record collection from spilling over into the study area.

Any parent, boy, or girl who can drive a nail can make the music bench. Almost any room has a corner big enough to fit it

in. Here are the step-by-step directions.

Just follow the cutting diagram and coded list to obtain accurate sizes for all the plywood parts. Use a large carpenter's square to assure accuracy and remember to allow for saw kerfs between parts.

Glue and nail the two sides to the edges of the bottom. Nail the top to the sides in the same manner.

Now paint the inside of the cabinet, including the back, before fastening, as well as both sides of the divider. It will be too difficult to do so after the cabinet is fully assembled. Apply two coats of paint. When paint is thoroughly dry, install divider and apply the back.

While enamel on the cabinet is drying, start construction of the pull-out record rack. Glue and nail the side and bottom together and then fasten the front as shown in the drawings.

Position three 7-inch records (45 rpm) on the rack and mark centers for dowel pegs that the records will hang on. Bore a hole through the back for three 1-inch flathead screws. The holes should be

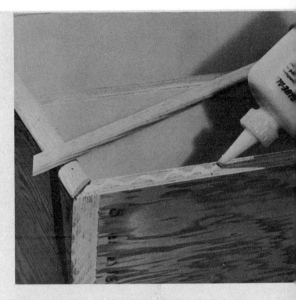

Make sure corners are even before you drive the nails. Glue all joints before nailing together.

Mitered corners for the front molding look best, and are easy to make with 45 degree angle cuts.

Give the bench a rich look by nailing a wooden edging around it. Corners are butted together.

Drive a nail through top, place the divider six inches from right edge and finish driving nail.

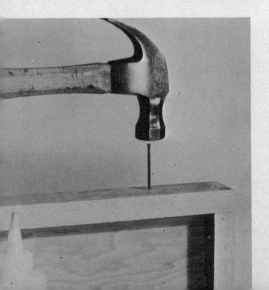

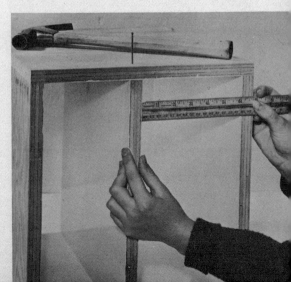

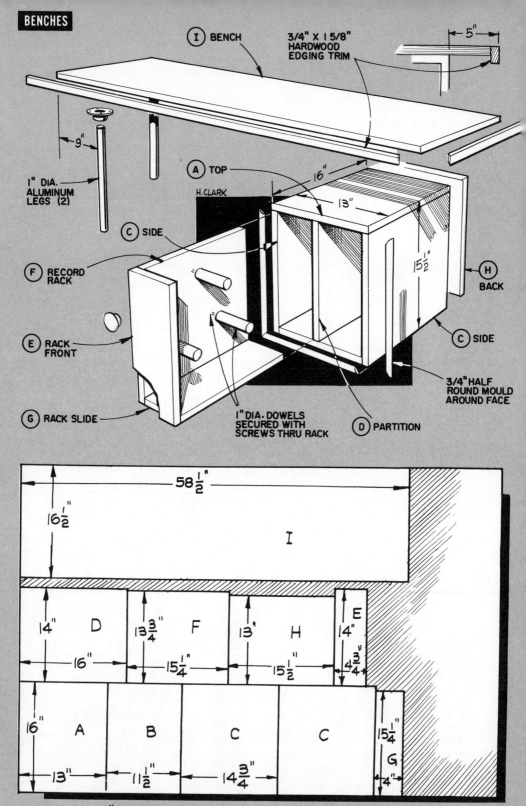

I BENCH

3/4" X 1 5/8" HARDWOOD EDGING TRIM

5"

9"

1" DIA. ALUMINUM LEGS (2)

A TOP

16"

13"

H. CLARK

15 1/2"

C SIDE

F RECORD RACK

H BACK

E RACK FRONT

C SIDE

G RACK SLIDE

1" DIA. DOWELS SECURED WITH SCREWS THRU RACK

D PARTITION

3/4" HALF ROUND MOULD AROUND FACE

58 1/2"

16 1/2"

I

14"   D   13 3/4"   F   13'   H   E

16"   15 1/4"   15 1/2"   14"

4 3/4"

16"   A   B   C   C   15 1/4"

13"   11 1/2"   14 3/4"   G

4"

3/4" X 4' X 6' PLYWOOD CUTTING DIAGRAM

Wooden dowels hold the 45 rpm records in a slide-out rack. Larger LP's fit into compartment, at right.

countersunk. Predrill pegs for screws and then twist the pegs holding the screws with a screwdriver until the pegs are held snug.

Fill nail holes and plywood edges with wood paste or spackle, and sand until smooth. Apply two coats of paint to record rack and pull, and then apply the final coat to the whole unit.

To make the bench, glue and nail the wood edging to previously cut plywood seat. First, the ends and then the front and back. Now turn the seat upside down and fasten the aluminum legs with screws through flanges. Position them at 9 inches from the end and as close to the front and back as possible. Apply a three-coat paint job—undercoater followed with two coats of finish in a semigloss enamel.

The bench rests on the cabinet without fastening. However, if you wish to fasten it, use 1¼-inch flathead screws driven through top of cabinet into the bench. •

Telephone Bench

Well-styled phone stand and seat will give conversation in comfort

If there's the usual scramble for the telephone when it rings at your house, your phone deserves a handsome piece of furniture so it can stand the traffic gracefully.

This bench combines simplicity with pleasant styling. It has a welded wrought-iron frame and a roomy fir plywood seat. There's a smaller, elevated base at one end for the phone itself, with plenty of room for a note pad. The handy man at your address can build this graceful phone bench.

Construction

First you'll need the special metal framework shown in the drawing. Weld it up yourself if you have the shop facilities. If you don't have welding equipment, cut and bend the parts and take them out for welding. Or you can simply take this plan to a welding shop and ask them to build the frame. They will usually drill the metal frame for screws and file the welds for clean neat joints.

Now smooth the wrought iron with fine abrasive cloth. Then give the metal one coat of metal primer and at least two coats of flat black enamel.

Next, lay out and cut the plywood seat and shelf. True up the cut edges with 1-0 sandpaper wrapped around a block. Carefully notch the edges of the plywood seat to fit between the metal shelf supports with a rattail file. The seat will have to be tilted to wedge it into position. When it's fitted, fasten it to the framework with round-head screws.

Bevel strips of hardwood to make molding for the seat and shelf. If a circular saw is not available, bevel them with a cabinetmaker's smoothing plane. Miter this molding and then frame both seat and shelf panels, nailing and gluing the hardwood to the edges of the plywood.

Fasten the telephone shelf to the metal supports with screws. Then fill nail holes with wood filler and round all sharp corners and edges of the molding with 3-0 sandpaper.

After applying enamel undercoater to seat and shelf, follow with two coats of semigloss enamel. Protect metal frame with masking tape. If desired, a natural finish may be applied to hardwood edging. To do this, mask out edging while enamel is being applied. Remove masking and finish edging with one coat clear resin sealer followed by two coats of eggshell varnish. •

Give the telephone instrument a place of its own by building this simple bench. The wrought-iron frame is solid enough for two people, if necessary.

IRON ROD BENDING DIAGRAM

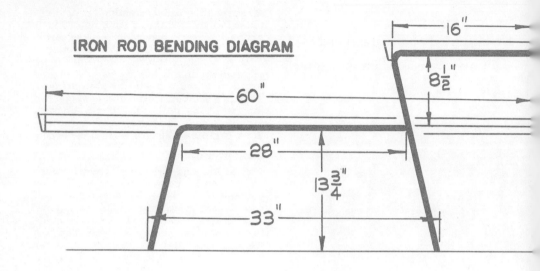

16"

8 ½"

60"

28"

13 ¾"

33"

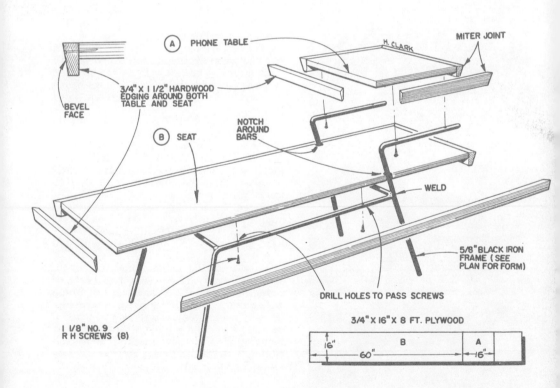

A PHONE TABLE

H. CLARK

MITER JOINT

3/4" X 1 1/2" HARDWOOD EDGING AROUND BOTH TABLE AND SEAT

BEVEL FACE

NOTCH AROUND BARS

B SEAT

WELD

5/8" BLACK IRON FRAME (SEE PLAN FOR FORM)

DRILL HOLES TO PASS SCREWS

1 1/8" NO. 9 R H SCREWS (8)

3/4" X 16" X 8 FT. PLYWOOD

16"

B

A

60"

16"

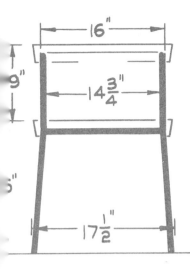

Attach the wrought-iron framework to the long plywood panel with screws through the iron. Framework is a welding project.

Fit telephone shelf to the frame. It is easier to attach molding strips to this piece before final assembly. (See diagram on opposite page.)

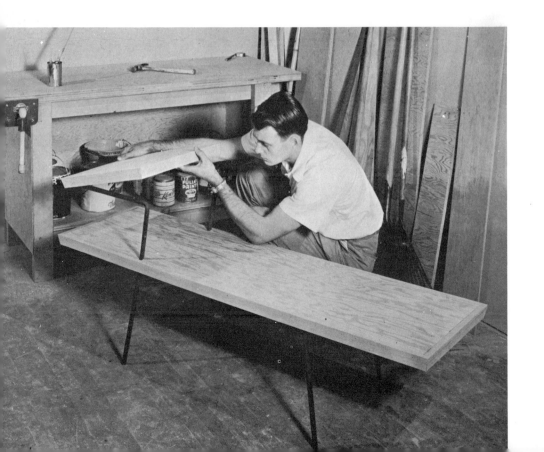

SLAT BENCH AND CABINET

By Peter Gowland

The simple design of this useful and attractive piece of furniture makes it as easy to build as it is to look at.

RECORD STORAGE or magazine rack, even hi-fi or radio can be housed in this modern design by Don Staska. Unique slat bench lends an interesting contrast in texture to the cabinet.

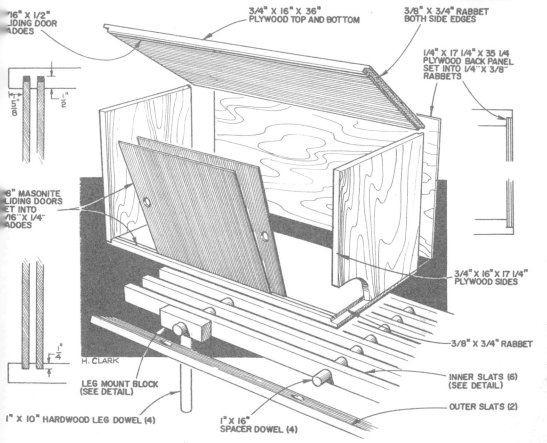

3/16" X 1/2"
SLIDING DOOR
DADOES

3/4" X 16" X 36"
PLYWOOD TOP AND BOTTOM

3/8" X 3/4" RABBET
BOTH SIDE EDGES

1/4" X 17 1/4" X 35 1/4"
PLYWOOD BACK PANEL
SET INTO 1/4" X 3/8"
RABBETS

5/8" 1/2"

1/8" MASONITE
SLIDING DOORS
SET INTO
3/16" X 1/4"
DADOES

3/4" X 16" X 17 1/4"
PLYWOOD SIDES

3/8" X 3/4" RABBET

1/4" 1/4"

H. CLARK

LEG MOUNT BLOCK
(SEE DETAIL)

INNER SLATS (6)
(SEE DETAIL)

OUTER SLATS (2)

1" X 10" HARDWOOD LEG DOWEL (4)

1" X 16"
SPACER DOWEL (4)

CONSTRUCTION DETAILS OF both cabinet and bench are shown above. Note simple sliding door construction in which Masonite panels fit into the grooves in top and bottom.

A PROJECT that can be easily made in the average home workshop, this bench and cabinet are made of simple components which, for the would-be home craftsman who does not have a workshop, can be obtained at most lumberyards, cut to size and milled as required; the only other tools necessary are the basic things found in most homes—some glue, a hammer, some elbow grease and adequate enthusiasm.

When completed, the bench can be stained or painted as desired; the doors can be painted a bright color for a bit of accent. Shelves or trays can be added to the cabinet to add to its usefulness. Use the cabinet for record storage or to hold magazines. •

MATERIALS LAID OUT and ready to assemble include eight 1x2 six-feet-long slats with one-inch holes drilled on 18-inch centers, beginning nine inches in from either end.

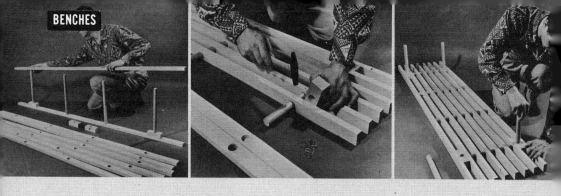

BEGIN ASSEMBLING BENCH by inserting four spacer dowels with one 2x2 spacer block located at either end of bench. Assemble additional slats over the dowels. Use remaining spacer blocks as a guide for assembling slats as shown. Hold slats in place with nails.

FINISHED BENCH is now ready for varnish, paint or stain. A good idea would be to give all pieces a coat of finishing material before assembly due to relative inaccessability of inside areas. Cut and groove all cabinet pieces as shown above. Doors are 1/8-inch Masonite, each 14 inches high, 8 inches wide. Sides, top and bottom are 3/4-inch plywood rabbeted as shown. Note dado cuts for sliding doors. Top dadoes cut deeper for assembly.

ASSEMBLE CABINET SIDES, top and bottom panels using glue and one-inch brads. Note that a square is used to properly line up side panels. Countersink nail heads, fill, sand before finishing. The 1/4-inch plywood backing is now set into rabbeted area and fastened in place.

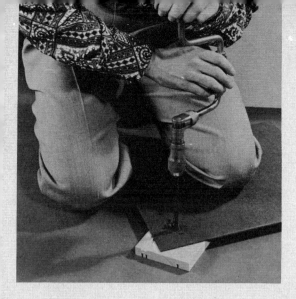

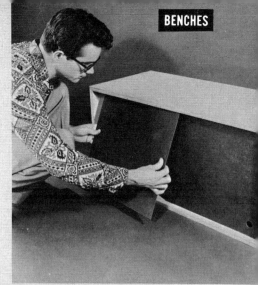

CAREFULLY DRILL ½-inch round hole in bottom corners of each sliding door for finger pulls. Use wood backing.

DADO CUTS FOR sliding doors are ½-inch deep on top piece, ¼-inch deep on bottom, permits easy assembly and removal.

FINISHED CABINET is simply set on one end of the bench and finished to suit. Cabinet, of course, can be set on either end.

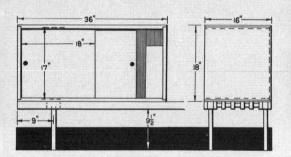

USE HARDWOOD for slats and bench construction in general for n e c e s s a r y strength, softer wood in this design would simply not hold up. Further construction details are shown above and at right. For a final decorative touch, paint doors a bright color to accent. Colorful toss pillows can be set on the bench to complement the doors. Bench can be used as a table to hold plants, magazines or books as desired.

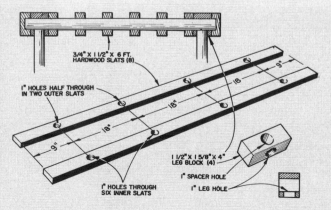

3/4" X 1 1/2" X 6 FT. HARDWOOD SLATS (8)

1" HOLES HALF THROUGH IN TWO OUTER SLATS

1 1/2" X 1 5/8" X 4" LEG BLOCK (4)

1" SPACER HOLE

1" LEG HOLE

1" HOLES THROUGH SIX INNER SLATS

BICYCLE RACK

Make this six-bike

rack without threading

a single piece of pipe!

by John Michaels

SLIP on some fittings and tighten setscrews. Outside of cutting tubing and pipe to length, that's all that's required to build this rack which holds up to six bikes—and it's a great thing to have on the premises when Junior's bike brigade comes calling.

The fittings which make assembly so easy are manufactured by the John Hosking Co., 1704 Howland Place, Cincinnati 23, Ohio, and are sold through hardware outlets. Instead of interior threads, they have setscrews housed in diamond-shaped bosses and these screws are simply turned down on the pipe or tubing. The company makes a complete line of fittings for all types of pipe and tube structures and the handyman can now do a professional job without cutting a single thread. In fact, with the adjustable elbows, tees and other fittings in the line, bending of the pipe or tubing isn't even necessary.

To make the rack, 1-inch and ¾-inch O.D. galvanized iron pipe is first cut to size with a pipe cutter. In the 1-inch piping, you'll need four 36-inch, four 12-inch and two 21½-inch lengths; in ¾-inch pipe, you'll need six 24-inch lengths. After drilling $1\frac{3}{16}$-inch holes in the horizontal center sections, spacing them as indicated on the drawing, you just work from the bottom up, slipping on fittings and tightening screws.

BASE of rack is assembled first. Piping doesn't have to be threaded for fittings.

SPACER PIPES fit into holes in the larger pipes and then the top elbows are secured.

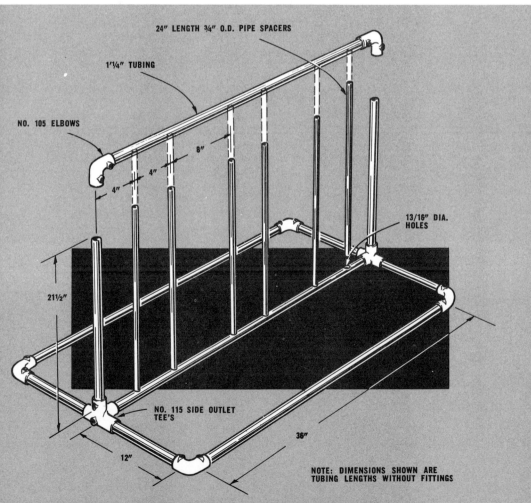

24" LENGTH ¾" O.D. PIPE SPACERS

1'¼" TUBING

NO. 105 ELBOWS

8"

4"

4"

4"

13/16" DIA. HOLES

21½"

NO. 115 SIDE OUTLET TEE'S

36"

12"

NOTE: DIMENSIONS SHOWN ARE TUBING LENGTHS WITHOUT FITTINGS

359

BIRD BATH

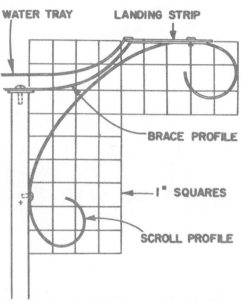

WATER TRAY   LANDING STRIP

BRACE PROFILE

1" SQUARES

SCROLL PROFILE

THE wide "landing strip" of this bird bath is an open invitation to any winged visitor to your garden. Its copper and brass construction will last indefinitely, actually improving with age.

For the water pan, turn a wood form to the final shape, then put the form and a piece of 22 ga. copper, 10-in. diameter, onto a metal or wood lathe. Complete the spinning with a shaped hardwood tool, braced against the tool post. Mutton tallow may be used as a lubricant. To finish, polish and lacquer to prevent tarnishing.—*C. A. Martin*

A wood block is turned to make a form, or "solid chuck," for the copper water pan.

Using a lathe, copper is spun against the form with help of a shaped hardwood tool.

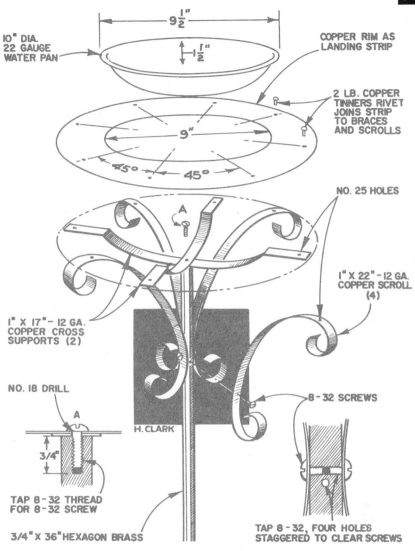

10" DIA. 22 GAUGE WATER PAN

9½"

1½"

COPPER RIM AS LANDING STRIP

2 LB. COPPER TINNERS RIVET JOINS STRIP TO BRACES AND SCROLLS

9"

45°   45°

NO. 25 HOLES

A

1" X 22" - 12 GA. COPPER SCROLL (4)

1" X 17" - 12 GA. COPPER CROSS SUPPORTS (2)

H. CLARK

NO. 18 DRILL

A

3/4"

TAP 8-32 THREAD FOR 8-32 SCREW

3/4" X 36" HEXAGON BRASS

8-32 SCREWS

TAP 8-32, FOUR HOLES STAGGERED TO CLEAR SCREWS

All copper scrollwork can easily be bent with a Metl-Former or around a cylinder.

Brass screws attach scrolls to center post, after they are riveted onto landing strip.

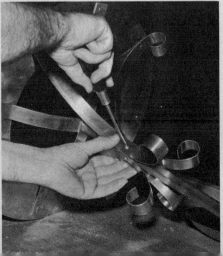

HOW TO BUILD A DOCK

Here's an easy project that'll make waterfront living more fun.

IF you're handy with a welder, you'll find it a relatively simple task to build a durable metal dock that will be the envy of your neighbors and a joy to use. If you don't weld, you can simply cut all the pieces to size and hire a welder to assemble the dock. It'll still be inexpensive.

A metal dock such as this one overcomes all the disadvantages of wooden ones: it is sturdy, lighter in weight than a wooden dock of the same strength, it's durable and can be hauled ashore during the winter months. This last point is very important

in northern areas, where high water and ice can wreck a wooden dock in no time. Another advantage of this unit is that, being mounted on wheels, it can be easily moved in or out as the depth of the lake varies during the season.

Keep construction costs down to a minimum by shopping around at a junkyard and by making reasonable substitutions of materials. The dock shown in the photographs was built for less than $35. Naturally, the length of the dock, and its height at the outer end, may be varied from

PERMANENT in appearance, the dock may be taken out of water in winter, to avoid damage.

CROSSBAR welded one foot in from the shore end of the frame is for attaching to a trailer hitch.

the plan to suit the terrain of your site.

Our 40-foot unit is made as follows. The bed pieces consist of two 20-foot lengths of angle iron on each side, each pair butt-welded at the middle. These are set with their angles to the inside so the 2x4-inch pieces for the walk will fit into them. After the bed pieces are butt-welded, they are turned over on level ground and the box frames, made of 2-inch angle iron, 12x40 inches, are welded at the outer end and the center. The center frame is placed over the butt weld.

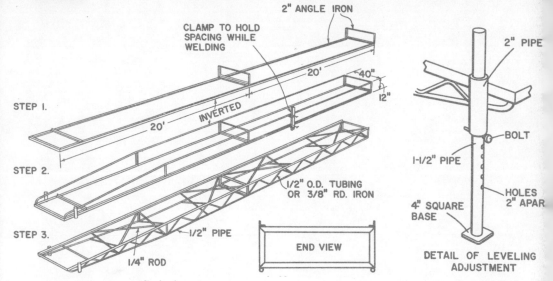

One 40-inch piece of 2-inch angle iron is welded across the shore end, and another about a foot in from it. The latter is for attaching to a trailer hitch in order to tow the dock to its waterfront site. This completes the top surface (step 1 above).

Next comes the construction of the side framing. Half-inch pipe (about ¾-inch outside diameter) is used for the lower edge. Space it 12 inches from the angle iron, except at the shore end where it is tapered up to meet the angle iron framing. Butt weld any joints in the pipe, then weld it to the box frames at the shore end and the center. At the point where the side frame bends upward to meet the end (10 feet from the end), weld in a piece of ½-inch pipe, 12 inches long, as a spacer. You now have what is seen in step 2 of the first diagram.

Mark off the angle iron frame about every 30 inches for the zig-zag diagonal bracing and do the same on the pipe, making the markings on the pipe halfway between the marks on the angle iron. You'll have to make the markings closer together at the shore end, where the angle iron and pipe frames taper together, to maintain the constant angle of the bracing.

On the dock shown, steel tubing with ½-inch outside diameter was used for the bracing. Since an acetylene welder was used for the job, the tubing was bent and welded as the work went along. If such tubing is not available, ⅜-inch round iron will do as well. You will notice, in the photographs, that vertical braces were also used in the end section on one side; this isn't really necessary, as the frame is quite rigid without them.

About 6 inches in from the shore end, weld an 8-inch section of 2-inch pipe on each side (see diagram No. 2 for details). These will support the pieces of 1½-inch pipe which serve as legs for leveling the shore end of the dock. Weld some diagonal cross-rods into the frame, for additional rigidity (as seen in step 3 of the first diagram), and you are ready to construct the outer end.

A front axle, wheels and tires of an old car can generally be picked up for $10 or so. After determining the necessary height of the dock at the site where you intend to use it, weld the uprights and braces between the axle and frame, and then put in diagonal cross-rods to prevent side sway (as in diagram No. 3).

If you'd like to add a rail and ladder, follow the details of diagram No. 4.

Next step is to file off any sharp edges, remove any accumulations of rust, and dress up your dock with a coat or two of aluminum paint.

The only wooden part of this project is the walk. This is made in sections that can be easily handled (as shown in diagram No. 5). Make the sections, as shown, and treat them with a commercial wood preservative for longer life. When the wood is dry, you may give the walk a few coats of aluminum paint, too. Finally, simply lay the sections of the walk down on the angle of the angle-iron frame.

At this point, you've got a dock with wheels. Now fill your old tires with a solution of calcium chloride and water, as is done with farm tractor tires. Then attach the trailer hitch, back your car up to it and haul it off to your lakeside retreat. But one final word of caution: as you're ambling down the road with this metal monster behind you, don't try any sharp turns! •

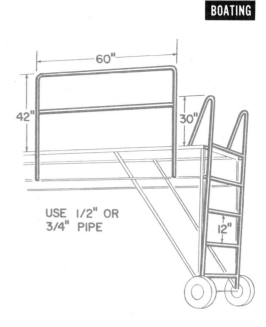

60"

42"

30"

USE 1/2" OR
3/4" PIPE

12"

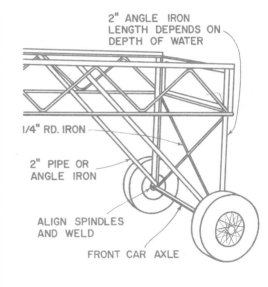

2" ANGLE IRON
LENGTH DEPENDS ON
DEPTH OF WATER

1/4" RD. IRON

2" PIPE OR
ANGLE IRON

ALIGN SPINDLES
AND WELD

FRONT CAR AXLE

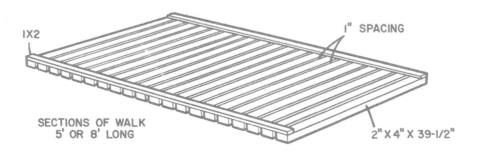

1X2

1" SPACING

SECTIONS OF WALK
5' OR 8' LONG

2" X 4" X 39-1/2"

Portable Marine Railway

IF ice and the elements in your neighborhood conspire to treat permanent marine railways with disrespect, thwart them by constructing this portable affair. It can be set up in the spring on any sloping beach near your camp or cottage and taken down for storage in the fall.

The winch has an 8:1 reduction and two cranks, so it will handle a boat as big as 20 feet long. It consists of a 2-in. 10-diametrical-pitch spur gear on a ¾-in. steel shaft and a 16-in. 10-diametrical-pitch spur gear on a 1-in. shaft. Both shafts are set in bronze bushings. The cranks go on the upper shaft and a 3-in. drum is added to the lower shaft. Fit the large gear with a pawl and install some means of locking the crank when not in use to prevent children from catching their fingers in the gears.

Use 8-foot track sections, as shown, if your beach is uneven; longer units can be employed where the slope is fairly straight. Each section consists of two 2x4-in. tracks, four 2x4-in. cross members, and two 1x4-in. rails. Spike these members together, cut half-laps in the ends of the tracks, and bore holes through the laps to take the ½-in. coupling bolts.

The first cross member on the track section farthest up on shore is made from a 2x6-in. timber. Note that it extends out beyond the sides of the section so stakes can be driven to anchor the railway. Build a 2x6-in. frame above this cross member to take the winch. After assembling the winch, bore oil holes through the framework and bushings.

Construct the car from 2x6-in. timbers and brace it with 1x4-in. stock. Additionally brace it with two pieces of ⅛x3-in. flatbar crossed in the center and secured to the undersides of the 2x6-in. stringers. Assemble with bolts. Four 6-in. bronze-bushed wheels without flanges are required. Mount them on ¾-in. steel axles and set the axles in bronze bushings in the car stringers.

The ends of the car that is detailed here are for a shallow-draft V-bottom boat. Shape them to conform with the bottom of the boat and pad with canvas or old fire hose. If your boat has a deep keel, a higher cradle will have to be constructed. For a round-bottom craft, make paper or cardboard patterns of the bottom curves, transfer the shapes to 2x12-in. stock, and band-saw the pieces to fit.

—*Hi Sibley.* •

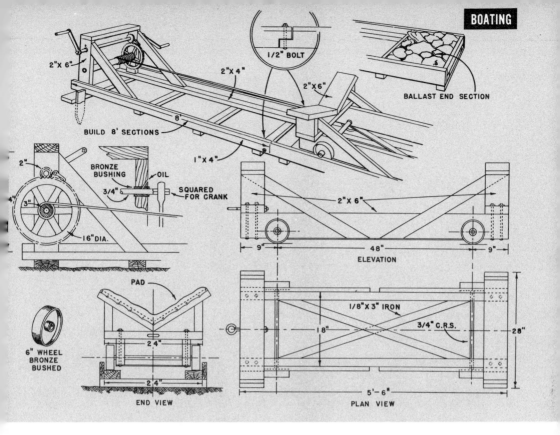

2" X 6"

1/2" BOLT

BALLAST END SECTION

2" X 4"

2" X 6"

BUILD 8' SECTIONS

8'

1" X 4"

2"

BRONZE BUSHING

OIL

SQUARED FOR CRANK

3/4"

3"

16" DIA.

2" X 6"

9"

48"

9"

ELEVATION

PAD

6" WHEEL BRONZE BUSHED

1/8" X 3" IRON

3/4" C.R.S.

18"

28"

2 4"

2 4"

END VIEW

5'-6"

PLAN VIEW

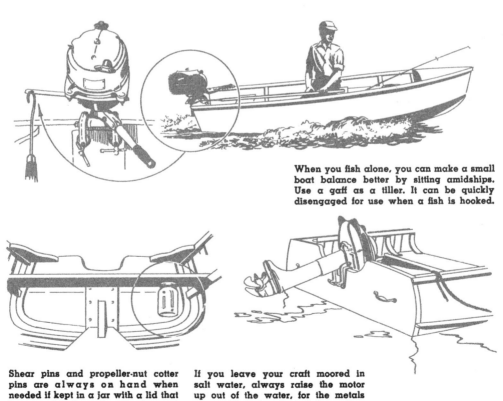

When you fish alone, you can make a small boat balance better by sitting amidships. Use a gaff as a tiller. It can be quickly disengaged for use when a fish is hooked.

Shear pins and propeller-nut cotter pins are always on hand when needed if kept in a jar with a lid that is screwed to the underside of a seat.

If you leave your craft moored in salt water, always raise the motor up out of the water, for the metals are subject to electrolytic action.

367

Tilting Trailer

By Joseph Adams

Save trouble and toil by building a trailer that makes it easy to launch and haul out your boat.

FEATURING a tilting cradle and a winch, this small boat trailer can be built with tools possessed by practically every handy man. Some welding is required, but that can be done at a local shop while the bulk of the work progresses. When the job is done, the wooden frame will even outlast steel, especially around salt water.

Before starting construction, procure the front end of a small car, preferably a Crosley. Have the axle and tie rod cut, pieced out and welded so that the width between wheels is 54 inches. Have one spindle welded in position, leaving the other free for adjustment.

While the welding is being done, buy the lumber. Get a good grade of hardwood, such as fir (not spruce). The stock should be clear and straight-grained, without large knots.

Start construction with the box frame. The sides, as noted in the drawing, are six feet long and the width is determined by the location of the springs on the widened axle. The front spring shackles are fixed and each one is attached with two $\frac{5}{16}$-inch bolts so that the axle will be at the center of the frame. The rear shackles float in rubber bushings, so bore a large enough hole in each side piece to take the bushing and the bolt. The whole frame can then be assembled with two $\frac{5}{16}$-inch bolts through each joint.

The stationary yoke is the one to which the trailer hitch is attached. The other, which fits inside, is the tilting

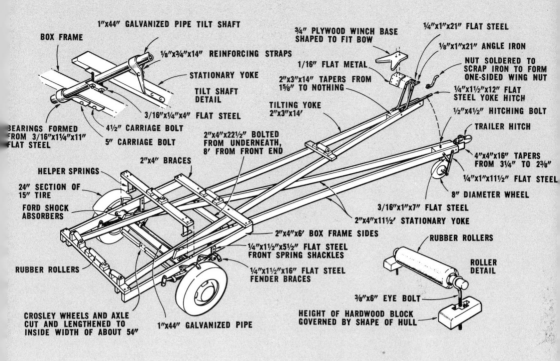

1"x44" GALVANIZED PIPE TILT SHAFT

BOX FRAME

¾" PLYWOOD WINCH BASE SHAPED TO FIT BOW

¼"x1"x21" FLAT STEEL

⅛"x¾"x14" REINFORCING STRAPS

⅛"x1"x21" ANGLE IRON

STATIONARY YOKE

1/16" FLAT METAL

NUT SOLDERED TO SCRAP IRON TO FORM ONE-SIDED WING NUT

TILT SHAFT DETAIL

2"x3"x14" TAPERS FROM 1⅝" TO NOTHING

¼"x1½"x12" FLAT STEEL YOKE HITCH

TILTING YOKE 2"x3"x14'

3/16"x¼"x4" FLAT STEEL

½"x4½" HITCHING BOLT

TRAILER HITCH

BEARINGS FORMED FROM 3/16"x1¼"x11" FLAT STEEL

4½" CARRIAGE BOLT

5" CARRIAGE BOLT

2"x4"x22½" BOLTED FROM UNDERNEATH, 8' FROM FRONT END

4"x4"x16" TAPERS FROM 3¼" TO 2⅜"

2"x4" BRACES

¼"x1"x11½" FLAT STEEL

HELPER SPRINGS

8" DIAMETER WHEEL

24" SECTION OF 15" TIRE

3/16"x1"x7" FLAT STEEL

FORD SHOCK ABSORBERS

2"x4"x11½' STATIONARY YOKE

2"x4"x6' BOX FRAME SIDES

RUBBER ROLLERS

¼"x1½"x5½" FLAT STEEL FRONT SPRING SHACKLES

ROLLER DETAIL

RUBBER ROLLERS

¼"x1½"x16" FLAT STEEL FENDER BRACES

CROSLEY WHEELS AND AXLE CUT AND LENGTHENED TO INSIDE WIDTH OF ABOUT 54"

1"x44" GALVANIZED PIPE

⅜"x6" EYE BOLT

HEIGHT OF HARDWOOD BLOCK GOVERNED BY SHAPE OF HULL

yoke. To make the stationary yoke, attach two 11½-foot 2x4's to the tapered nose piece with three ⅜x7½-inch bolts, allowing four inches of the nose piece to project at the front for the trailer hitch. (Two of the bolts will later hold the front wheel assembly.) The yoke is then spread, with a crosspiece on the underside, so that the ends fall five inches inside the box frame, leaving room to mount the shock absorbers.

The stationary yoke is secured to a one-inch pipe which rotates in strap bearings attached to the undersides of the box frame seven inches in front of the axle. To keep the pipe from shifting, place a large washer on each end and secure it with a cotter pin.

The tilting yoke is made the same way as the stationary yoke except that the nose piece tapers to zero at the front end and both the nuts and heads of three $\frac{5}{16}$-inch bolts used to attach the sides are countersunk. A crosspiece,

Top of yoke is raised 14 in. above ground by a wheel of 8-in. diameter.

Nut with welded handle is removed when you have to raise tilting yoke.

which bears a roller, is bolted to the top of this yoke about three feet from the end; it should be wide enough so that the ends rest on the stationary yoke. Bear in mind that the spread of the yoke should be such that there is a 1/8-inch space between the yokes when they are fitted together. (This also applies at the nose.)

The winch mount is made up of two pieces of 21-inch angle iron and one piece of flat steel. Two inches from each end, a V is cut in one side of the angle iron. The ends are then bent down at 45° angles and welded. Cut one side of the angle iron away at the lower end so that you will have a flat base. The two members are secured ten inches from the end of the tilting yoke with two $\frac{5}{16}$-inch bolts. The center piece of flat steel is bent to rise more abruptly and meet with the outside members. Beneath this center piece, another piece of flat steel is bolted; it extends to hitch the two yokes together and the forward end is secured to a bolt in the stationary yoke with a one-sided wing nut made as illustrated. The top of the mount is reinforced with a piece of flat metal and a 3/4-inch piece of plywood extended in a fork to fit the bow of the boat. When the winch mount is installed, the tilting yoke can be attached to the undersides of the box frame crosspieces with two $\frac{5}{16}$-inch bolts at each joint.

The front wheel, which is attached to the stationary yoke, is a small industrial type, eight inches in diameter. The flat steel supports are drilled to accept two of the bolts through the nose piece. When the installation is complete, the top of the yoke should be 14 inches above the ground.

Six wringer rollers are used on the box frame and tilting yoke. Five of these are

Plywood piece, cut to bow contour, is secured between winch and mount.

Pipe to which stationary yoke is fastened turns in two bearings made of flat steel.

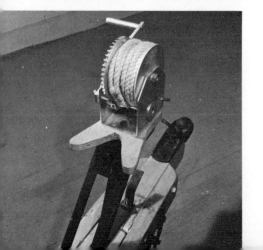

cut in half; the center back one is used full width. They are installed as shown in the drawing, with the outside ones tilted to fit the contour of the boat bottom.

If a Crosley front end is employed, shock absorbers from a Model A Ford will literally fall in place as illustrated. We found the Crosley springs a little light for a heavy, 16-foot runabout loaded down with a 35-hp motor and all the equipment needed for a week end camping and fishing trip. To remedy this, helper springs which bear on the axle were added. They are nothing more than heavy valve springs from a large truck motor slipped over $\frac{7}{16}$x7-inch bolts and secured with pieces of flat steel. Each assembly is attached to the center crosspiece so that the bottom is about one inch above the axle. For additional compression, light car valve springs can be inserted within the heavy springs.

Fender braces are first fashioned from light metal. Once the shape is determined, they are duplicated in the heavier steel indicated on the drawing. The heavy steel can be bent with a 20-ounce hammer in a large vise without heating or strenuous effort. Clamp the braces in position, remove the wheel and bolt them in place.

The fenders are cut from tires slightly larger than those used for the trailer. We found that 15-inch tires have just the right contour for the 12-inch Crosley wheels. Simply outline the tire section with grease and cut with a heavy pocket knife. The grease lubricates the blade. Attach each fender to the brackets with four stove bolts, using washers under the heads.

After being given a coat of paint, your trailer is finished. You'll find that it looks as good as any on the road.

The stationary yoke is fastened to pipe with bolts and steel straps.

Helper springs are made of flat steel, truck valve springs and bolts.

Fender supports are shown clamped to frame for a check on shape and location.

Shock absorber from Model A Ford fits fine on the Crosley axle.

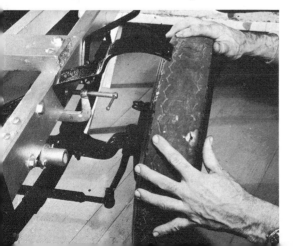

Top Off Your Boat

Even at top speed of 25 mph, canvas is snug, doesn't flap.

SMALL boat owners who want relief from a blistering sun or some measure of shelter in a light shower can make this canvas top for less than $15. The only materials needed are some 12-oz. canvas, two 10-ft. lengths of aluminum tubing or electrical conduit, some aluminum clothesline and odds and ends of hardware.

The frames are bent at the width of

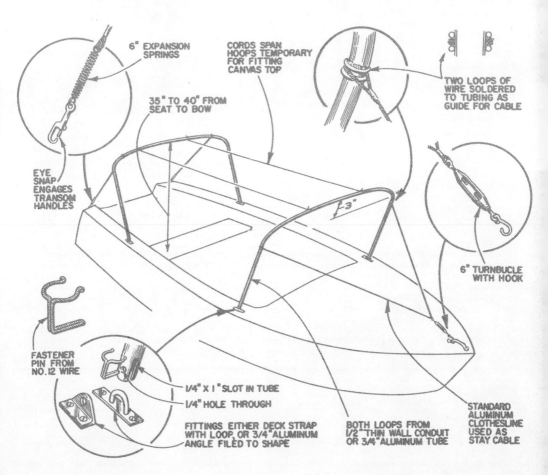

6" EXPANSION SPRINGS

CORDS SPAN HOOPS TEMPORARY FOR FITTING CANVAS TOP

TWO LOOPS OF WIRE SOLDERED TO TUBING AS GUIDE FOR CABLE

35" TO 40" FROM SEAT TO BOW

EYE SNAP ENGAGES TRANSOM HANDLES

3"

6" TURNBUCLE WITH HOOK

FASTENER PIN FROM NO. 12 WIRE

1/4" X 1" SLOT IN TUBE

1/4" HOLE THROUGH

FITTINGS EITHER DECK STRAP WITH LOOP, OR 3/4" ALUMINUM ANGLE FILED TO SHAPE

BOTH LOOPS FROM 1/2" THIN WALL CONDUIT OR 3/4" ALUMINUM TUBE

STANDARD ALUMINUM CLOTHESLINE USED AS STAY CABLE

Use full-size template for conduit bending;
use sand if no bending tool is available.

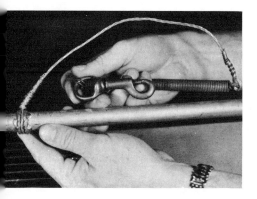
To allow cable to move on conduit, solder
two washers on conduit with cable between.

Brackets made from aluminum angles hold
conduits. Bend fasteners from No. 12 wire.

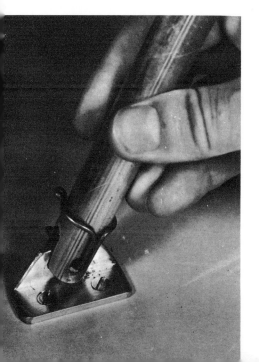

Canvas is hemmed at both ends, then slipped
onto the conduit. Note slight bow across top.

the boat and it's best to do the job on a
bending tool. If you don't have one yourself, the dealer who sells the conduit probably has. Leave the conduit long at both
sides, then position each frame on the boat
and cut off the ends at the proper length for
passenger comfort and motor access.

Tie the two frames together on the boat
and determine the right slant for the best
appearance. When they're in the right
position, the required lengths of cable and
canvas can be measured.

When the canvas is cut to size, a waterproofing agent is applied. Then the sides
are hemmed and 2-in. looped hems are
made at the ends so that the conduit slips
through easily.

A word of caution: Don't take chances
with any kind of top on a small boat if you
intend to use it on open water that can
really rough up. When the weather looks
as if it will go bad, best take the top down.
Waves lifting the boat and wind under the
canvas will work to flip you over. If rain
is accompanied by wind and waves, the
canvas offers no shelter anyway. •

Caulking, Painting and

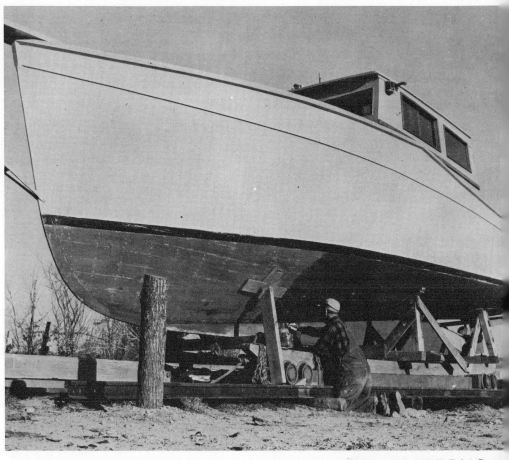

Photos courtesy Petit Paint Co.

It is easy to scrape an old surface after paint remover has caused it to bubble up.

Plastic composition wood can fill this hole. Sand the area first and wipe away all dirt.

Hull Repair

By John Kingdon

THE man who intends to fit out and paint his own boat in the spring must have the patience of a Missouri farmer who owns a stubborn mule. Fifty per cent of his efforts will be put forth in scrubbing, patching and sanding before the paint brush comes into play. And, as if this were not enough, the rest of his activity will be punctuated with eight to 48-hour waiting periods between coats of paint.

All this is not meant to sour you on painting, but merely to point up the basic fact that a first-rate paint job can be achieved only if you get an early start and proceed slowly.

Actually, fitting out need not be a chore. If the skipper, the first mate and all the little mates pitch into the work, it can be satisfying family fun. And when the craft slides into the water, all concerned will feel happy because of a good job well done.

Also, don't ignore your friends when making up your work gang. They'll expect to be invited aboard during the summer, so there's no reason why they shouldn't help out in the spring.

For best maintenance, you should paint your boat each year. If the previous paint job was a good one, this yearly maintenance chore will be relatively simple. But if last year's paint was haphazardly applied or if the finish is checked and cracking, resign yourself to a major reconditioning.

The first thing to do is to remove all hardware and other detachable items such as seats, locker doors, hatch covers and the like. Next, using a mild detergent, hot water and a fairly stiff brush, scrub off dirt, oil, grease and algae; then hose the boat off and let it dry.

Reconditioning

When everything's dry, inspect the hull to decide whether or not it needs a major refinishing or just repainting. If the finish is in good shape, all that remains is to sand the hull lightly and to apply a coat or two of paint and/or varnish. But if the surface is afflicted with large checked or cracked areas, the boat will have to be refinished completely, which means removing all the old paint down to the bare wood and starting from scratch.

For a major reconditioning, here are the steps to follow:

1. Soften the old paint. You can use a paste-type paint remover, blowtorch, infra-red lamp or electric flatiron.

If paint remover is employed, two applications may be needed to cut through the many layers of old paint. After scraping the paint and remover off, wash down the wood with alcohol or turpentine to take off wax left by the remover.

Spread plastic dough generously in crevices (left) with wide-bladed knife. For shallow marks (center), apply a plastic surfacer. Large, marked areas (right) call for glazing compound.

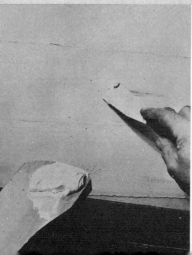

When sanding by hand, abrasive will work better if a 2x3-in. wooden block is used.

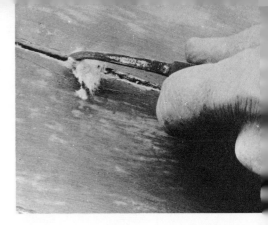

To make a new seam, use a spike to rake out old seam filler and caulking cotton.

The blowtorch is quick but dangerous. If you have never handled one before, take a lesson in its use from an experienced operator: never bring it into play without having a fire extinguisher handy. Above all, don't ever use paint remover and then follow up immediately with a blowtorch. Some paint removers are so highly flammable that a surface treated with one of them will burst into flame if a blowtorch is brought to bear on it.

The infra-red lamp is slower but safer. This lamp or bulb is the type employed to alleviate stiff muscles. It can be used in any portable electric fixture that has a reflector. Hold the lamp about one inch from the surface until blisters form, then move it along slowly and follow it with a scraper.

The electric flatiron is the slowest but perhaps the most easily come by of all the paint softeners. To use, simply "iron" the paint until the surface is soft. Work but a small area at a time.

2. Remove the soft paint. Various kinds of scrapers are available. Of these, the most useful is the scraping knife, which looks like a broad-bladed putty knife. Also needed are a cabinet scraper, which has a working edge at each end, and a triangular scraper with a wooden handle. Care must be taken when using the latter to avoid digging into the wood with the points. To remove stubborn traces of paint and to clean out cracks, employ a stiff wire brush.

For raking out old seam compound sharpen and bend over the tang of an old flat file. (The tang is the slender projecting shank that fits into the wooden handle.) Bend the tang by heating it to a cherry red and hammer-ing it to quarter-circle shape over a steel rod held in a vise. When the tang is cool, file or grind it to a chisel point. Then reharden it by heating it again to a cherry red and plunging it in cold water.

3. If any hull repairs are needed, now's the time for them to be done. If you are not an expert woodworker, it's best to leave major jobs to the boat-yard or someone experienced in such work. Never try to do work on your craft which is beyond your honest capacity. Replacing the deck or putting in new planks, for example, involves special knowledge and hours of really tough, backbreaking labor. They are tasks for the professional.

But there are some repairs that are easily made. As an example, look at a metal rowlock socket. Probably you never gave it a thought, but this insignificant fitting is constantly exposed. Water seeps in at the joint between it and the wood in which it is set and stays there. In time the wood rots and one day, when you put a little extra pep into a stroke, the fastenings let go, causing the entire socket to give way. Unless you're good at sculling, you may find yourself in a bad spot. How much simpler it would have been to install new fastenings or new wood beforehand.

And what holds true for the rowlock socket is also valid for such common deck fitting as chocks, cleats and bitts. Often, all that's needed to restore one of these fittings to first-class condition is to replace the wood screws with through bolts, washers and nuts.

Perhaps such things as a rub rail, a seat or a false stem may need replacing. When removing one of these parts, it

Roll new cotton into a seam with a caulking wheel or tap it in with a caulking iron.

Finish topside seams with generous amount of seam compound; let dry 24 to 28 hours.

is usually possible to cut off stubborn nails by shoving a hacksaw blade (without its frame) into the joint and sawing back and forth. This is preferable to ripping the part off and possibly damaging sound members in the process.

Or if the part is screwed in place, don't mangle the screw with a screwdriver. Instead, use a brace with a screwdriver bit, bearing down on the handle and giving the crank short, sharp jabs. Much greater force can be applied with the brace than with a screwdriver, and, since the blade is firmly held in the slot, it can't jump out.

The old part can be used as a pattern when laying out its replacement. When installing the new part, use marine glue or paint to coat all surfaces that will be hidden. If new screws go in hard, rub them with beeswax or paraffin. Don't used soap, it contains ingredients that will attack the metal.

4. Smooth the hull down. If it is planked with conventional wood, merely sand it. If it is planked with fir plywood, apply a coat of sealer such as Firzite and let it dry before doing any sanding. Never attempt to sand bare plywood; you'll only cut into the soft wood, accentuating the wild grain. Don't use a clear sealer on plywood that is to be painted. Instead, get the white type which contains a pigment that makes it a first coat of paint as well as a sealer.

There are five abrasive minerals commonly used for sandpaper. Three—flint, garnet and emery—are natural minerals; the other two—aluminum oxide and silicon carbide—are synthetics. The synthetics are much the stronger and longer-lasting.

Flint is the most generally used abrasive mineral. It is, however, the softest and has the shortest cutting life.

Garnet is reddish-brown in color and produces satisfactory results with a minimum of labor.

Emery is a black mineral with rounded, granular surfaces. Although it is a relatively dull cutting agent, it is an excellent abrasive for removing rust and corrosion from metal surfaces.

Aluminum oxide is gray-brown in color. It makes an excellent sandpaper for both metal and wood.

Silicon carbide is shiny black. It is the hardest and sharpest of all the sandpaper abrasives.

The most suitable of these for your purpose is either garnet or aluminum oxide. For rough sanding, use No. 1-50. For removing small imperfections and light scratches, employ No. 1/0 (80). And for a fine surface, finish up with No. 3/0 (100).

Sanding by hand is tiring. For this reason, the use of an electric sander is advised. If you don't have one, it can probably be rented from a nearby hardware store. Four kinds are manufactured: reciprocating (or vibrating), orbital, belt and disk. The last two are the fastest, but must be used with care by the amateur if he is to avoid scarring the surface by sanding too long in one spot.

5. Brush on a coat of sealer, let it dry, then sand it down.

6. Fill all dents and gashes with plastic composition wood or one of the other similar compounds on the market. Also putty all nail and screw holes and, if your boat is the type that requires it, apply seam compound. Don't apply any of these compounds before putting on the first coat of sealer. If you do, the

oils in the compounds may be so thoroughly absorbed by the wood that the compounds will dry and fall out.

Some conventionally planked boats require caulking cotton in their seams as well as seam compound. To find out whether or not such caulking is in good shape, pull out a little. If it looks black, the fibers are probably rotten and should be replaced. Either the tang of an old file (as previously described) or a putty knife can be used to dig it out.

Before putting in the new caulking flow paint into the seam to make the cotton stick better. Don't hammer the caulking in as if you were caulking a canal boat. The planking of the average small boat is too thin to be beaten with a caulking mallet. Besides, all that's needed, even in the most wide-open seams, is a thin strand of cotton. When the boat is put into the water, the wood will swell and take up the slack.

So instead of pounding in masses of caulking material, merely roll the strand of cotton into place. The tool to use is called a caulking wheel. If you can't get one, you can use a putty knife to push the cotton into the seams.

To leave room for the seam compound, keep the caulking a little below the surface. When adding the compound, finish off the seam so that it is slightly hollow. When the wood swells, this will level up.

7. Brush on another coat of sealer, let it dry, then sand just enough to take off the fuzz. For sanding here and between other coats, worn sandpaper is ideal.

8. Brush on a coat of marine undercoater and, after allowing it to dry thoroughly, sand vigorously, but not so vigorously that you get down to the wood. For a super-smooth finish, apply another coat of the undercoater. If you're going to paint your craft some color other than white, it's wise to tint this second undercoat in the desired color. Sand this coat just hard enough to provide a "tooth" to hold the finish paint.

9. Finish with two coats of marine paint, allowing the first to dry and sanding lightly before applying the second. Brush the paint in well. Two thin coats are much better than one thick one. More than two coats, on the other hand, can be bad because too many coats may get so heavy that they will break down under their own weight. This is especially important on canvas surfaces. Thick paint makes canvas crack, and once a crack starts there is no way of getting rid of it except to put down new canvas, which is a major job.

To estimate the paint remover, paint and varnish required (in gallons per coat), use the following formulas:

Paint Remover. One gallon will soften 200 square ft.

For Topsides. Multiply the length of the boat by the freeboard at the highest point and then by 1.5. Divide by 400.

For Bottoms. Multiply the length of the boat on the water line by the draft and then by 3.5. Divide by 400.

For Decks. Multiply the length of the boat by the beam and then by .75. Deduct the areas of all deck openings and cabins and then divide by 400.

For Housetops. Multiply the length by the width and divide by 400.

For Spars. Multiply the length of each by its greatest diameter (in feet or fractions thereof) and then multiply the result by 2.5 and divide by 400.

Your labor is now done. Don't, however, put the boat into the water and immediately go tearing off. Allow her several days after launching to swell up properly. Otherwise some of your carefully placed caulking and seam compound may work loose, causing a leak that can last all summer. Or the dry wood may work back and forth so much around the fastenings that the fastening holes will be forced into oval shapes, which means that even when the wood does swell the fastenings will be loose.

An alternate method of swelling the wood is to run a hose in your boat a few days before launching. At first the water will probably run out through the seams just about as fast as it comes in, but the boat will slowly start to swell up. Inside of 24 hours, she should be fairly tight. And by the time you are ready to launch, your troubles will be over.

Painting Tips

Know what materials you need for each job and make sure you have them on hand.

During the long spring evenings or on rainy days, when you cannot work on the boat, plan to do some small jobs—such as varnishing hatches, spars, furniture, etc.—at home.

To save time in cleaning up dripping

paint and retouching, always start at the top and work down. This means that if your boat is rightside up, you should finish the gunwales first and the bottom last; if the boat is upside down, you should finish the bottom first and the gunwales last.

Paint backward, working from a dry section into the wet paint of a previously coated area.

Brush vigorously to spread the paint evenly and eliminate all bubbles.

Work with strong, steady strokes.

Do not constantly rebrush a coated area.

Paint with the grain.

Paint on a dry, calm day only. Avoid windy weather and its resulting dust.

The ideal temperature for painting is between 60° and 85°. Don't paint when the weather is excessively hot. The hot sun may induce such rapid evaporation of some of the solvents that a skin will be formed on the surface with the remaining solvent imprisoned under it. This will inevitably cause "gas blistering." If you *must* paint in extremely hot weather, you can partially guard against this rapid evaporation by always working on the shady side, away from sun.

Start early in the day and quit early enough so the paint can begin to set before the evening dew forms.

It pays to use only good marine paint. Choose a well-known brand and then carefully follow the manufacturer's recommendations (printed on the label affixed to the can). Use only the thinner recommended by the manufacturer. And never mix the paints or varnishes of different manufacturers; their formulas may clash.

Stir the paint thoroughly before each application to mix the pigment with the liquid portion. The proper way to do this is to pour part of the liquid into another can and then to stir the pigment up from the bottom into the remaining liquid. When the mixture becomes absolutely smooth, stir in the extra liquid and then pour everything from one can to the other several times. If the paint has been opened and used before, a skin will have formed over it. All traces of this should be removed by straining the paint through cheesecloth.

Don't shake varnish or enamel. Doing so creates air bubbles that are hard to brush out. •

Use toxic seam cement under anti-fouling bottom paints. It repels marine organisms.

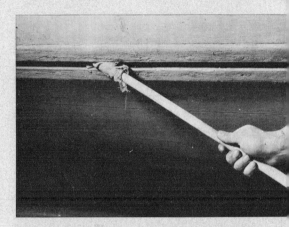

Using cloth tacked on a stick, coat centerboard trunk interior with anti-fouling paint.

Brush out paint vigorously; spread evenly. Two thin coats are better than one thick one.

Race Your Sailboat

Sailing close-hauled in a spanking breeze is enjoyment in itself, but the ultimate in satisfaction comes from racing against another craft.

By Tom Griberg

BESIDES a fleet of boats manned by enthusiastic crews, three things are required to stage a sailboat race: first, a means of signalling the start; second, a means of marking the course; and third, a set of clearly understood rules to govern the boats.

A gun shot has long been accepted as the signal for the start of a race. For this purpose, a noisy little cannon can easily be constructed from an old single-shot shotgun.

Remove and discard the stock, forearm and trigger guard and cut the barrel to a length of 11 inches. Then braze a ¼-in. nut to the bottom of the breech 2½ in. ahead of the fitting which

on the ends for cotter pins and pushed through the hole in the tailstock. The cast iron wheels are 8 in. in diameter and may be obtained at a farm implement supply store. Short pieces of ½-in. tubing are cut to fit over the axle between the wheels and the tailstock. Rubber tires are made from lengths of hose and can be held in place by threading a piece of screen door spring through the hose. The spring is cut slightly shorter than the circumference of the wheel.

Blank shotgun shells should be used in the cannon. Three shots are generally fired to start a race. We find that a five-minute warning gun followed by a one-minute warning gun and finally, the starting gun, works out very well.

To construct an efficient marker, first fasten two ¾x3x36-in. pieces of scrap lumber together in the center with a simple cross lap joint. Over the joint nail a 9x9-in. square of ¾-in. wood. This piece serves to strengthen the joint and also to give greater support to the 12-in. piece of ½-in. wall conduit which holds the flagstaff. The conduit should be forced into a drive fit hole which is drilled at center of the cross. Pinch the bottom end of conduit together so flagstaff will not slip all the way through.

Slip the ends of the cross arms through the handles of four one-gallon varnish cans. Fasten them in place with ¾-in. roundhead screws. In the center of the cross, on the underside, install a large screweye for the anchor line. Since the varnish cans will rust if not protected, give the entire construction several coats of bright-colored enamel. For flags, hem 18-in. squares of red or yellow cloth and attach them to 36-in. lengths of ½-in. dowel with copper tacks.

Lay out a race course and anchor a marker at each turn. The length of the course is optional and while a triangular course is desirable, it is not mandatory. If possible, make the first leg of the course such that the boats can be sailed close-hauled since this makes the boats easier to control at the starting line. If a series of races are planned, the markers can be left out, provided they do not interfere with navigation. Just before race, the flags can be inserted in the conduit holders.

was originally used in screwing the barrel to the forearm. Next, secure a pair of 2-in. bolts to fit the threads on these fittings. Finally, drill a small hole through the end of the trigger to take a stout cord which will serve as a lanyard.

From 2-in. oak or maple, bandsaw a tailstock as shown in the drawing and bore the required holes. Note that the end of the tailstock is hollowed out and filled with lead so that the gun will not be nose heavy. The top end should also be hollowed out to fit the underside of the breech. Then the shotgun is bolted to the tailstock.

The ½-in. diameter axle is cut from a 9-in. length of cold rolled steel, drilled

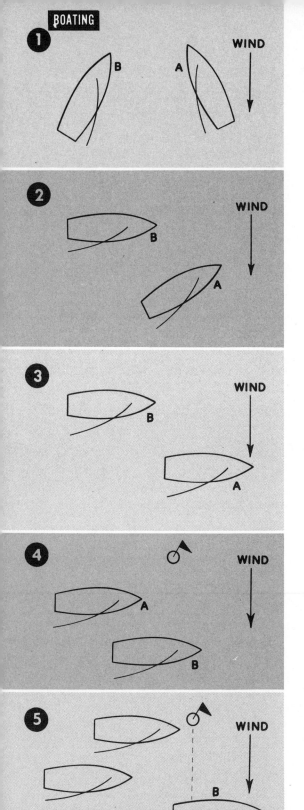

1 WIND

B A

2 WIND

B

A

3 WIND

B

A

4 WIND

A

B

5 WIND

B

Cross pieces are simply slid under handles of cans and fastened in place with screws.

Inexpensive course marker is easily built from one-gallon cans, lumber and conduit.

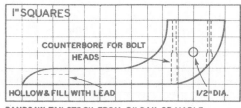

1" SQUARES

COUNTERBORE FOR BOLT HEADS

HOLLOW & FILL WITH LEAD

1/2" DIA.

BANDSAW TAILSTOCK FROM 2" OAK OR MAPLE

Nut brazed to underside of breech takes one of two bolts which secure tailstock.

Hardwood tailstock is bored for ½-in. dia. axle made from 9-in. length of steel rod.

Shotgun and tailstock assembly is fitted on axle. Tailstock is weighted with lead.

The completed cannon. Blank shells make a loud report easily heard in all the boats.

Rules are necessary in sailboat **racing**, as in any sport, to give everybody an equal chance to win. However, in the case of sailboat racing, rules are even more necessary for the safety of the boats and crews. Five important rules which can be used for the governing of an enjoyable series of races are illustrated in the diagrams. Drawing 1 shows two boats converging on opposite tacks. The boat on starboard tack (wind over starboard rail with boom to port) has the right of way. Boat B on port tack must give way to boat A on starboard tack.

When converging courses on the same tack (Drawing 2) the windward boat must keep clear. Boat B to windward must give way to boat A to leeward.

When on parallel courses on the same tack (Drawing 3) the overtaking boat B must give way to the overtaken boat A.

When making a turn, an overtaking boat may demand buoy room provided he has established an overlap on the overtaken boat (Drawing 4). Boat B must give boat A room to make the turn. This rule does not apply at the starting line.

A boat crossing the starting line ahead of the starting gun (Drawing 5) must turn and recross the line. During this time he must give way to all other boats. Boat B is at fault and must turn back.

If more complete rules are desired they may be obtained for a small fee from the North American Yacht Racing Union, 37 West 44th Street, New York City, N. Y. •

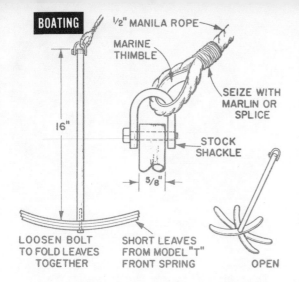

½" MANILA ROPE

MARINE THIMBLE

SEIZE WITH MARLIN OR SPLICE

STOCK SHACKLE

16"

5/8"

LOOSEN BOLT TO FOLD LEAVES TOGETHER

SHORT LEAVES FROM MODEL "T" FRONT SPRING

OPEN

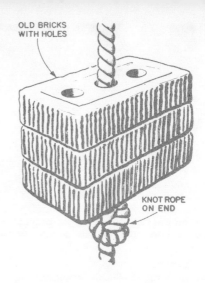

OLD BRICKS WITH HOLES

KNOT ROPE ON END

Use ⅝-in.-dia. cold rolled steel for shank and standard shackle with 11/16-in. opening for this light anchor. Drill holes for shackle and retaining bolts in lower end with latter being tapped. When loosened, spring leaves fold up for easy stowing.

A length of rope with two or three knots in one end and several discarded bricks can be made into a very satisfactory anchor. Put unknotted end of the rope through holes in the bricks, slide them down to knot, and anchor is ready to use.

BOATING TIPS

Lacking the regular wooden barrel available at boat yards for testing and cleaning outboards, use a large, clean ash can for this purpose. Remove plug from motor, then pull motor through slowly to circulate water through intake manifold, etc.

You can build and install a white stern light for your boat, as shown below. The removable staff is locked in its socket by a spring clip and pin. The dimensions below can be altered to bring the light directly over the boat's center line.

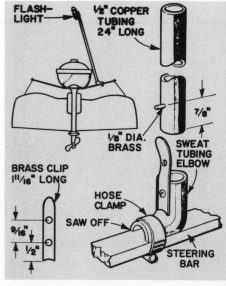

FLASH-LIGHT

½" COPPER TUBING 24" LONG

7/8"

1/8" DIA. BRASS

SWEAT TUBING ELBOW

BRASS CLIP 1¹¹/₁₆" LONG

HOSE CLAMP

9/16"

SAW OFF

½"

STEERING BAR